Identity
Interrupted

Meriam Rodriguez

Library of Congress Control Number: 2021907802
ISBN: 978-0-578-88798-2

Anniversary paperback edition June 2021

Book design by Meriam Rodriguez
Cover Image by Paulina Barasch
ISBN: 978-0-578-88798-2 (paperback)
ISBN: 978-0-578-88799-9 (ebook)

www.meriamrodriguez.com

This is dedicated to the lovers that have lost themselves while trying to be loved.

Inspired by true events.

PARTY GIRL

The planet must be off-axis again. It's the only logical explanation that pops into mind while resurrecting from the dead and falling through a vertigo spiral – *too many tequila shots last night.* I reach over for my cell phone to see what time it is, but it's not on the nightstand. And the spin in my brain isn't allowing me to send out a search party for it.

My mother, a short bulldog of a woman, is yelling at my father downstairs. There's a rage that dwells in her bones, causing her to spontaneously combust daily. This current aggression taken out on my dad is because I came home at 6 a.m. It's a chaotic symphony of racked dishes, cabinets getting slammed, and weighted footsteps pacing back and forth below my room. By the time she makes it to my door, the storm is full speed.

"You can't keep living in my house like this!" she yells.

The vibration of her words puts pressure on my brain as the need to learn my limit screeches in with a hangover. I can tell by the beads of sweat forming on the tip of my nose, the flush in my fingertips, and the vertigo I mentioned earlier. Mami is now a blurred figure in the corner judging me.

I have some job interviews lined up for today. The first one started a few minutes ago. It doesn't look like I'll be making the others either, not the way I'm feeling.

Ugh! I promise never to drink again if you take this feeling away, I proclaim to the hangover gods.

My prayer goes unanswered. The alcohol sitting in

my stomach is now making its way back up. With-in seconds, I'm purging the spirits and memories of a night I can hardly remember. Shit. I can't think of any-thing after that fifth shot, which was around midnight. What happened after that?

My legs are unsteady as I wash my face and brush out the stale taste in my mouth. Mami takes my efforts as an opportunity to continue her rant.

"What you did this morning has to stop. You're an adult now," she says.

"This is what people my age do, ma!" I protest, knowing damn well I've been overdoing it since be-coming single again.

"They also work and pay bills."

"Can we please not do this right now? I don't feel good."

"Of course, you don't feel good. *¡Si estaba más bor-racha que el Diablo!*" she declares.

3

"Drunker than the devil" is her way of making me feel sinful when I drink too much. When she wants to put me down for smoking weed, she'll call me a *tecata*. She just doesn't get it. My mother was never a party girl. Her judgment of me comes from the fact that the wildest she ever got were wine coolers and drag races back in the day.

"All I'm saying is you better find a job and move out soon."

"Okay, ma. Fine. Please stop," I beg, my legs still wobbly.

Reading the expression on her face tells me there's more to say, but she retreats to the kitchen. Her voice bears calmer energy as I hear her venting to my aunt on the phone. Titi Chachi, her best audience, is always interested in hearing about my most recent offenses. They usually spend hours on the phone talking about family *bochinche* with my name in heavy rotation.

Titi calls me later in the day.

"Hi, twisted!" (Her term of endearment for my sexual preference.) "Are you still feeling sick?"

She then patronizes me for stressing my mother out. The intention is always hard to decipher between random jokes. I can never tell if she's serious or not.

"Why do you keep partying so much? You know your mother is a *loca*." she continues. "Besides, you can't find a husband if you're always on the streets."

"I think that's actually how a lot of women find their husbands, Titi." I snap back.

These talks lead to taboo remarks and questions about lesbian sex. Her lack of a filter makes it easy to express myself freely until she starts talking about what she would do with a hot actor from a *novela* or some cute doctor she met. Once the jokes get too dirty, I check out.

"All right, it was good talking to you."

She laughs at me.

"Too much?"

"Definitely too much. I love you, Titi. *Bendición*."

"*Que Dios te bendiga.* Bye."

Despite being angry at me, Mami makes a big pot of *sancocho*. This chunky stew is well known in the Latino community to be a cure-all, especially for my current state. After getting seconds, I feel like a brand-new person, and so does my mother. Her fury has eased as we all lounge in the *sala* with warm bellies and Monday night football. No matter how much trouble I get into or how many arguments we have, it's never long before my parents are spoiling me again.

Home is a small house in the South Bronx that they bought ten years ago through a local church's affordable housing program. They're not religious by any means. Mami is always daring God to come down himself if he has a problem with her ways. I usually take a few steps back when she does this, in case she gets struck by lightning. I know that's fucked up, but you don't test boundaries with the big guy like that.

My parents have been together since Papi returned from the Vietnam War. When I asked him to tell me their love story, he threw out a dad joke of her following him home one day, not the fairytale I was hoping to hear. Romantic or not, they've been married for thirty years, and it somehow works. You might even say they're living the American Dream, but I use their marriage as a marker for what I don't want in a relationship.

My older brother, Kelvin Jr., has just gotten back from serving boot camp in the Marines. It was his dream since he was a little boy in the cadets. Once he was there, though, he hated it.

"The drill instructors are pricks," he told us the night he came back.

I think the real reason was that he missed his girl-friend, Vero.

My younger sister, Winnie, is "kid goals." Her teachers love her, and she never gives my parents any trouble. Her favorite pastime is re-enacting dance scenes from classic films. The most practiced one being the iconic jump in *Dirty Dancing*. It includes Winnie using the coffee table as a dance partner. She gets just enough momentum to catch the perfect slide across the top and holds the pose.

Then there's me. No matter what my mother tells you, I am a constant delight. Yeah, sure, growing up, my teachers always complained about me, but that was because I was in a Catholic school that expected us to be robots. One teacher told me my charm would buy me fifteen minutes, and I was doomed after that. She was a nun, but they can be assholes, too. I personally think they should be allowed to have sex, so their frustrations don't get taken out on students. Despite all of this, I turned out okay.

If it wasn't for my mother, we'd be living in a suburban town in Jersey somewhere. Papi didn't want to raise us in the Bronx. It was her that found out about the program and convinced him to stay close to our grandmothers.

Mamá, my maternal grandmother, lives ten minutes away, behind Yankee Stadium. *Abuela*, my paternal grandmother, lives twenty minutes away in Washington Heights.

We're close enough if either of them needs my parents. Papi agreed, and it was a done deal. My parents are "ride or die" like that with each other and everyone else. You can call them with an emergency any hour of the day, and they'll drop what they're doing to get to you.

Growing up, we'd all get packed in the car for spontaneous visits to Titi Chachi in Connecticut and help her with things around the house. They would also lend the family car to neighbors and wire money to family in Puerto Rico, even when they struggled. Mami is a magician at balancing the budget on my father's sole income. The agreement between them was always straightforward; he earns the money, and she holds down the fort. Like I said, they make it work.

When we first moved here, I remember being intimidated by the tall buildings that surrounded our little cluster of cookie-cutter houses. I never knew what projects were until then. For some reason, I don't remember seeing any when we lived up by Fordham Road. These massive housing complexes didn't exist in the small towns of Connecticut that we were shipped off to every summer, either. They're aggressive, towering over us like bullies. This house looks extra tiny in comparison, but it's home, our home.

I didn't get much done today, but tomorrow I'll find a job and become a productive member of society. For months now, I have spent most of my nights at clubs, drinking and dancing until dawn. Papi being the bankroll to my party girl ways.

"Don't tell your mother," he always whispers to me.

"I won't, I promise."

Then a pinky swear to make it official.

There's nothing more transcendent than being on a dance floor full of sexy people, feeling ourselves while letting the music take us away.

The abandonment.

The sweat and grinding.

Bodies bouncing to the beat.

I love this city's club scene. It's my favorite escape, but the real world is calling, and asking Papi for money is getting old. Quick. I feel ashamed every time I come to him, but all that matters in those moments is getting to the party.

After accepting the loss of my phone, I remember that I'm still clueless about what trouble last night brought us. It started with a pre-game at Sammy's — that's my best friend, my closest confidant, and the funniest person I know. She doesn't fall into our society's standard of "good looking," but I swear she can have anyone with her charm and sense of humor. I've seen it with my own eyes. Sometimes, she even outshines me when flirting with girls, but I feel like a proud poppa seeing her in action.

Everything started with a bottle of Jose Cuervo before heading out to our favorite club, Krash. A bottle of tequila goes a long way when you don't have a job and are trying to save money on drinks. By the time we left, things were already pretty blurry. Hopefully, Sammy remembers what happened. Either way, it's time to get my life together. Tomorrow will be another day of arguments if I'm not out looking for work.

A sudden urge to create a plan of action baits me back to my room. Down the Craigslist rabbit hole, I go.

Uninspired, my search leads me to other job forums, boards, and sites that come to mind. I don't meet the qualifications for most of them asking for some experience or a degree.

I then pull out a copy of the *Village Voice* from my backpack. The Voice is a free newspaper that has everything you can think of in it. Men seeking women, men seeking men, weight loss programs, HIV testing, and ways to explore all types of fantasies. Everything weird, fun, lucrative, and dangerous in this city has six degrees of separation to these pages, from concerts to sex workers, to how and where to donate your eggs for $8,000. I thought about doing this once, but they only wanted White and Asian donors. I wonder if it's because these two demographics tend to be in higher income and performance brackets or because Hispanics and Blacks don't have those traits that society idolizes. Diabetes in my family would've canceled me out, anyway, so it was a short trip down that road.

I keep reading my options:

GUITAR LESSONS

Maybe I can be a rock star! Wait, I don't like leather pants or eyeliner. And I can't play an instrument or sing for the life of me. Next.

WORK FROM HOME STUFFING ENVELOPES

No, thank you! Paper cuts hurt like hell.

BIKE MESSENGERS

I write down the contact information for five messenger listings.

WAITRESS NEEDED - WILL TRAIN

I'm not crazy about this section, but I write down a few places that sound cool. The pages that follow catch my interest, even though it's not quite what I'm looking to do. They include ads for everything you can think of for swingers, voyeurs, Trans women, chicks with dicks, Gals Next Door, big booty-little boobs, vice-versa, a gay male dating site, something called *Putas Pussy Village*, and "real women from Europe." There are pictures of unreasonably gorgeous-looking people attached to each listing. I wonder how many of them have workers that really look this hot, now hyper-aware that my curiosity has officially triggered.

The next page has smaller boxes that look similar to the classifieds, except these are for jobs in the sex industry.

EXOTIC DANCERS AND SEXY BARTENDERS FOR STRIP CLUBS

Another box is hiring for Shiatsu and Swedish massages. *Hmm, I bet happy endings are included.*

I shake my head, unamused with my frat-boy humor. Then a cryptic entry catches my attention:

TLC ROLEPLAY & FANTASY

Contact Becca @ 212-555-3842

(Btwn 11AM-6PM)

The force is strong with this one. It makes me linger. I'm not sure if it's the words "roleplay & fantasy" or because it's so vague, but reading them excites me.

What is this?

I peel myself away and read some others that are just weird and turn the page. The monthly horoscope is way off and has nothing to do with my current life – something about the coldest winters serving a higher purpose.

Ambition doesn't spark when your career options are bike messenger or waitress. Tomorrow is going to be a depressing day, but it's officially time to get back into the rat race.

JOB HUNTING

The pillow shields my face from jagged barbs of sun breaking through the curtains. There's a silence assuring me that everyone is gone for the day. Getting out of bed is more of a challenge with all of this quiet solitude.

Naturally, I end up in Papi's garden in the backyard. His small storage shed is the perfect place to hide away and smoke the good earth... *God's Lettuce*. Followed by meditation until the growl in my tummy sets me off-kilter for some munchies. A bowl of colorful marshmallow cereal satisfies the need for a sugar rush.

Whoever said potheads are lazy should do a study on me. Once I get that feeling of excitement in the pit of my stomach, I'm ready to make some calls. With the house phone in hand, I focus on my list. A couple of rings later, a man with a raspy smoker's voice picks up, then goes into a full coughing attack. He sounds like he's choking. I feel like I should do or say something to help, then consider hanging up but choose patience instead and wait. He finally clears his throat, drinks something, then tries to speak normally. I can tell the itch is still tickling his throat.

"Sorry 'bout that. Jaguar Courier, how can I help you?"

"Hi, yes. Are you okay?"

"Yeah, I'm fine. What can I do for you?" the man replies with an attitude. His misery crackles through the phone.

"I'm calling about the ad for bike messengers."

He starts coughing again, but this time it doesn't last as long.

"Do you have any experience?"

"No, but I do have a general knowledge of the city."

"Okay, what avenue divides east from west?"

"East from west? Um, Broadway?"

I'm not one hundred percent sure, but it sounds about right.

"No, 5th Avenue. Where does Madison Avenue begin and end?" he tries again.

I take a long pause, trying to buy myself some time. I have no idea what the answer is. I'm clearly not doing well here.

Think. Madison Avenue...

"Starts at 14th Street and ends at 138th?" I ask, guessing.

"Wrong. It starts at 23rd Street and ends at 138th. Sorry kid, two out of three gets you into the office for an interview. Study a map and call back when you think you've got it."

"Thank y--"

He hangs up mid-sentence. So much for Jaguar Courier.

I get a similar response on the next call.

"Some experience necessary, hon'."

There are still others to call, but rejection sucks, so I save face and move on. Twice in less than a couple of minutes is good enough for today. Looking back at my list, all the waitress positions are in-person interviews. Serving food is the last job I want. The moment I have some entitled brat talking down to me, I'll be flicking pennies at them.

Okay, relax and think about it. It's your best option for a quick hire and fast money. You could be working by tomorrow. My pep talk works until the roleplay and fantasy ad comes to mind again. It's currently 10:18 a.m., and they said to call between 11 a.m. and 6 p.m.

The thought lingers as I get dressed.

My outfit consists of the only skirt in my closet, paired with a white button-down shirt. Mami made me buy it last month for my cousin Maddie's birthday party. Her exact demand was, "I want you to look like a girl for once." Of course, Papi defended me, and it broke into an all-out war.

Guess who won?

It doesn't matter because I eventually wore the damn skirt to keep the peace between them.

My hair gets tied back into a high ponytail. A classic, professional look, I think to myself. Yeah, professional. For waitressing and maybe a "roleplay & fantasy" job. I search the newspaper for that little square and take down the name and phone number. When I call, a girl named Ana answers.

"Becca isn't here yet, but you can come by after 2 p.m. The address is 20 Irving Place, by Union Square."

I catch the silver-studded unicorn that is the 5-train

downtown. Halfway into the city, I change my mind and decide not to go. There was nothing shared with me other than the address. I still have no clue what this place is.

How far does the fantasy go?

What if it's a setup to get young girls caught up in something more dangerous. Would it even be in print if it was something like human trafficking? That newspaper is pretty well known, and I'm sure I could defend myself if things got out of hand. I go back and forth between doubt and curiosity the entire ride.

My first stop is Giggles Bar & Grill. The manager, an overtly flamboyant Colombian man in his late forties, whose bald head and bright smile give him a Buddha-like quality, hires me on the spot.

"My name is Marco Antonio," he says with a Sofía Vergara-like accent. "I keep this place running. Without me, it would fall apart."

Marco is highly entertaining as he embodies the archetype of pageantry often related to gay men. Every syllable is enunciated with the theatrics of a Broadway performer.

"We have the best after-work parties, and our lunch crowd is mostly regulars." He continues while looking me up and down. "Wear black pants and a black top. Anything else gets too dirty, too quickly. Will you need to be trained, or do you have any experience, miss…"

His whirlwind energy has me so caught up that I have yet to introduce myself properly.

"Oh, sorry. Solei. Solei Romero."

"Okay, Solei Romero! Introducing yourself like James Bond and shit," he fans himself with a menu dramatically. "I like you. You would be a good fit for Giggles. Here, fill out these forms. I'll be right back."

That was so much easier than I thought it would be. Marco and his energy feel like a lighthouse to my little lost ship. I do a happy dance as I fill out the paperwork. He returns a few minutes later with a black, pocketed apron and two notepads for taking orders.

"Can you come in tomorrow for training?"

"Yes, what time should I be here?"

"Be here at 10 a.m. I'll ask Toni, our head waitress, to train you. She's been with us the longest and is great at what she does. Bring I.D. and your social, so that I can put you on the payroll."

"Thank you so much, Marco. I appreciate it. I'll see you tomorrow."

I treat myself to wings and beer at a nearby restaurant's bar to celebrate. By the time I'm done, it's 2:20 p.m. The other interview I have lined up crosses my mind. I can't even visualize this mysterious place because I have no idea what it would look like.

Roleplay & Fantasy.

The two words have haunted me all afternoon. What if I go just to satisfy my curiosity? I don't have to commit to anything. It's just an interview. And at that very moment, against all of my common sense, I decide to go.

CRIMSON AND BLACK

The ride downtown lasts less than five minutes – not enough time to mentally prepare for this situation. A tug of war plays on in my head as I walk slower than usual. The option to turn back towards the train station hovers like the threat of an afternoon rainstorm. Knowing that I could change my mind at any moment pushes me to keep walking, but I almost miss the entrance tucked in between a deli and an electronics store. When I enter, I'm greeted by a frail, small-framed doorman smiling back at me.

"Good afternoon," he tips his hat and gestures towards the sign-in book sitting in front of him. "What floor?"

There's a visible change when I respond, "the fourth floor."

His smile fades and the kindness in his eyes has disappeared. I sign the log and thank him, to which he props open his newspaper and nods absently.

My hand trembles while calling the elevator. The awkward silence now shared between us echoes my heartbeat. Deep breaths help me relax, but my body remains clenched.

Ding

Finally.

The antique elevator has a gate that slides in and out of place for boarding. It clangs and rattles past each level. When I reach the fourth floor, it bounces into place as the outer door slams open. I slide the gate and slowly walk out, careful not to let my heels make noise.

A long, narrow hallway is lit by one bulb covered in dust. Directly in front of the elevator, there's concealed laughter and chitchat behind a black door. My only other option has an EXIT sign above it. I knock twice. The laughter stops. A clacking of heels turns away from the door. Then a loud buzzer invites me to step inside.

My heartbeat is now thumping against my temples like a drum. I'm surprised to see a front desk that looks like a counter at an indie record shop. A soft glow from the lighting has a *Red Light Special* tint and is a sharp contrast to the gloomy hallway. The beautiful girls behind the counter smile back at me. The shorter one looks like punk rock, Brittany Spears with streaks of pink in her bleach blonde hair. She reminds me of emo girls from high school. Dilated pupils covered in black eyeliner and glittering eyeshadow study me in the dark of the room. A black, spaghetti-string top exposes an excessively defined collar bone that hints at an eating disorder or heavy drug use.

On her right stands a taller girl. I should refer to her as a woman instead of a girl from the voluptuousness of her body. Large breasts fill every seam to the brim of her halter top. Thick thighs compress into a sheer mini skirt with chubby cheeks that betray her. Punk rock chick speaks first.

"Hi, I'm Becca."

"Nice to meet you. I'm Sol..." I stop myself from saying my full name, just in case.

"This is Anastasia. We call her Ana when clients aren't around."

"Yes, Ana. You're the one I spoke to earlier."

I shuffle in place, trying to contain the tide of anxiety overflowing within me.

"Do you have I.D.?"

"I do, but can I get more information first?"

I need to know what this place is before I start

showing anybody anything. They seem to understand my thought process as they nod back in unison.

"Can you wait in the first room on your left? I'll be with you in a few minutes."

A haze in the air gives the place an ethereal feeling. I generate a mental map of the layout – three doors on the left, two on the right, and, most importantly, an exit door at the end. When I step into the room, there's a long, rectangular-shaped mirror on the right wall and a black leather loveseat. As I step further into the space and settle in, a contraption facing the couch has all of my attention. If it wasn't in a place like this, I would guess it to be a dentist or barbershop chair. Given the environment, though, I'm pretty sure its purpose is more perverse.

The lighting, like the rest of this place, is dark. Both sides of the room have walls that don't reach the ceiling and leave a foot of open space between them. They're discussing phone calls on the other side. Anastasia gives a rundown of today's clients and their scheduled times as Becca informs her that she'll be done soon. Her footsteps walk in the opposite direction. I continue to study the room. There's a TV below the mirror and a set of VHS tapes.

The options include:

Dominant Nurses

House of Bondage

Latex Slaves

Big Gulp

The walls are a deep red, like crimson, with black borders. There's a coffee table with an empty ice bucket and ashtray on one corner. Sitting here, scrutinizing every detail, restores the curiosity that has been bubbling since this morning. The tap of Becca's shoes is now strutting towards me. She appears in the doorway and closes the door behind her.

"Sol, right?" she flashes a smile.

"Sol is short for Solei," I confess nervously.

"Sol, for short, is okay. You shouldn't use your real name here, anyway. It's best to use a 'character' name." She does air quotations with her fingers. "It can be a stripper type of name or a common name. We don't really give a shit."

"What exactly do you do here? I've never seen a place like this before."

"None of us know when we first come here, responding to that strange ad," she admits. "Basically, the owner Andy has a clientele he's built up over the years. These men and women have specific fantasies or fetishes that we help bring to life."

"Can you give me an example of what their fantasies are like?"

"One of our easiest clients is an old Jewish man, Ibrahim. He pays for thirty minute sessions for one of our girls to play with his beard and talk dirty to him. Once the time is up, we knock on the door, and you're done. When you leave the room, he does his thing and cleans up."

I can tell Becca has laid out this spiel many times before by her delivery.

"The rate for half an hour is $225, $125 of that goes to you. It doubles up nicely if the booking is extended," she continues.

I'm now doing the math in my head, in shock that I can make that much money playing with some random man's facial hair.

"Fair warning, though. Not all clients are that simple or respectful. Some will try to have sex with you, and they'll offer you a lot of money for it, too. Please do not have sex with any of the clients."

Becca's tone is weighted with authority. I swallow the lump in my throat and forget to breathe as I hang on her every word – riveted by these juicy details.

"They may decide not to pay once all is said and done. See, Andy is smart enough to charge the full amount at the time of booking," she explains. "Why? Because people switch up when their demons are silenced. If they decide to stiff you on that payment, I can't do anything about it. On top of the fact that it's illegal." she adds as an afterthought. "Have you ever worked for an escort service?"

"Like go on dates with old men?" I verify.

"Well, not exactly," she replies. "Escort services provide sex for money. Very rarely is it an actual date or outing with these men. It's prostitution with a prettier title and better-dressed pimps."

"Oh… Definitely not."

"Good. I wouldn't be able to hire you otherwise. Andy is strict about that. He believes it compromises our ability to turn down these offers if we've engaged in that business before."

She accurately interprets the shock on my face.

"Yeah, that's part of the culture here. Trusting that the next bitch isn't going to sell her coochie and mess it up for the rest of us."

"Has anyone ever been caught doing it?"

"Not while I've been working here, but Andy did tell me a story once. It ended with him having to bail out all the girls and shut down for six months. That's when he relocated here and had to start over."

"Do you know what happened to the girl that got caught?"

"I don't. I know she was charged, but that's about it."

"That's wild. Has a client ever tried to have sex with you?"

The thought of getting arrested for prostitution scares the shit out of me. My parents would kill me! My little sister Winnie would be heartbroken and confused.

She would never look at me the same. Kelvin would be next in line after my parents, ready to kill me again.

Becca's reply interrupts my thought tangent.

"Oh, absolutely. Most of us have been propositioned a few times, but as long as your answer is a firm no, you should be good. The only time it's not so easy is when you know they're not cops and are really trying to have sex with you. Those clients will be annoyingly persistent."

She points up to the opening in the walls.

"Andy chose this location purposely. I'm sure you've noticed."

"I was wondering why it was like that."

"The goal is to make sure there isn't too much privacy. It's an extra measure to minimize the temptation. The rest is up to us." Becca lowers her voice in confidence, "It's not always easy, either. Especially when business gets slow, or you spend too much money on partying and bad habits. Do you do drugs?"

"No," I lie.

"Okay, well. I have a weed guy, a coke guy, and another dude that sells acid tabs, 'shrooms, and X. Should you ever need it." she winks at me knowingly while I make a mental note for future reference.

Becca gets up and stands in front of the mirror. I watch her every move as she pulls out lipstick buried in her cleavage and reapplies.

"Follow me."

An otherworldly, *Twilight Zone* feeling passes through me as I peek into the other rooms. They're all identical to the first. Becca walks into the last door on the right. It's the only one that is different from the others. Silk scarves are draped over a Japanese-style room divider shielding a stand-up shower. Whips, straps, leather masks, and different sex toys serve as erotic art hanging from the walls.

"This is where we keep our bondage goodies for

clients that request domination and S&M. I'll spare you from those clients in your first few weeks. It can get pretty intense. There's an art to balancing the pain and pleasure that you will have to master. But you're welcome to sit in on sessions and see for yourself."

Her eyes shift to the center of the room, where there's another odd yet sinister-looking chair. It's a hybrid between a wheelchair and toilet seat with a metal pan underneath.

"What the hell?"

"It's called a BDSM toilet chair," she educates.

There's a wooden tablet laid out in front of it with four straps – one on each corner.

"What is this for?" The words barely make it out of my mouth.

"Andy designed this room for one of our top paying clients, Larry," Becca explains. "His fetish is the weirdest of them all... and the grossest."

"Really fucking weird."

My stomach turns. I hope I'm wrong, but I can already guess what the fetish is.

"I won't describe it to you. If you decide to take the job, that client will be in soon."

The energy in the hallway is charged with more mystery as we walk past the front desk. Ana is talking on the phone in a low voice when we walk towards the lounge area. The layout is a cozy living and dining room. Some of the girls are zombied on daytime television in one corner. Another pair sits at a black and white marble table on the right. One of them is reading; the other is doing homework. The afternoon sun is eclipsed by black velvet curtains cloaking another girl while she sleeps. A set of chairs round out in a circular formation next to the kitchen.

"These are the vampires of TLC," Becca announces.

They turn to size me up with a shared indifference.

One of the television girls gets annoyed and looks away.

"Hi, I'm Cheri."

"They call me Angel," another says.

Cheri maintains eye contact as I introduce myself. The rest of them say nothing and go back to what they were doing.

"This is Lola. Don't mind her. She's just a brat," she teases, referring to the vampire with the attitude. The girl laughs then throws a pillow at Cheri.

"Shut up. I'm not a brat. It's just, how are we supposed to make any money with so many girls here?"

"Andy likes to have a variety, so be nice," Becca interrupts.

"Yeah. It's not her fault Andy's greedy," Cheri adds.

"You're absolutely right."

She turns back to me. The lines of frustration on her face soften.

"Sorry about that… I'm usually not so rude."

The girls at the table are paying attention again.

"My name here is Baby."

"They call me Sugar," the other follows up.

Both of their noses go back into the books within seconds.

"The one sleeping back there is Brandy, after the singer, because she's her doppelgänger. Her words, not mine," Becca clarifies.

"We're always fully stocked with bottles of cheap wine to help us unwind." her cheesy choice of words bargains a melodic rhythm.

"The small kitchen is well equipped with a stainless-steel refrigerator, microwave, and watercooler. And wine, lots and lots of wine."

"It was nice to meet you," Cheri calls out as we exit the lounge.

I smile back at her.

"Yeah, same."

Is she flirting with me?

"So, what do you think? Are you interested in being a TLC girl?" Becca raises her left eyebrow with added drama.

"Call me crazy, but I wanna try it."

"That's what I'm talking about! Welcome to the crazy club, but now I need to see I.D."

"Oh, wait. I'm starting another job tomorrow in midtown. I don't know what my schedule is going to look like yet."

"We'll figure it out. Do you want to come here afterward?"

Becca hands me a business card.

"If you can't make it or change your mind, give us a courtesy call. This isn't a regular job where you get in trouble for calling out."

I promise to call if anything changes and get spit

out of their time warp. Stepping back into reality feels like jumping worlds. The lifeless hallway looks extra drab after the things I've seen hidden behind these walls.

I walk past the doorman and smile.

"See you tomorrow."

No response. This is going to be fun.

TRAINING DAY

The crack of dawn brings with it a harsh realization that today is my first day as a waitress. An internal struggle rages as the warmth of this cozy bed binds me against the need for a good alibi. My mother's detective skills are expert level. If I don't honestly believe what I'm telling her, she'll sniff out the lies. Despite this resistance, working at Giggles starts to grow on me as the day gets going, mainly because of Marco Antonio. He reminds me of the gay boys at Krash that we love to party with.

"Everyone, please say good morning to our newest server, Solei. She will be training with Toni." he introduces me during a morning staff meeting.

A petite, white woman with a boyish cut walks towards us with her hand extended and a monotonous greeting. Her jawbone tightens into a stress ball each time she chews her gum.

"Have you ever worked in a restaurant before?"

"No, I haven't." I swear she can smell the inexperience off me.

"Uh, huh," she continues, the wad of gum tucked into the interior of her cheek. "Well, lunch gets busy. I'll need you to stay out of my way when you see the tables filling up."

"Um, okay."

"Would you prefer I have someone else train her?" Marco interrupts.

"You know? That would be great, actually. I'm

not losing tips to train someone that won't even last 2 weeks."

Toni stares me up and down, then walks away like I slapped her momma or something. The heat on my cheeks and ears brandish embarrassment as I slip out of the way.

"Don't worry. I'll train you, miss honey," he turns his attention back to the staff. "If anyone sees Solei in need of assistance, please help her out."

"You, come with me."

We walk up a set of stairs to the second level of the restaurant. It hints at a New Orleans, French Quarter design with a second bar, room to dance, and a balcony overlooking the lower level.

"This is the employee coatroom. I'm the only one who has a key, so your things are safe here." Marco takes me into a closet-sized room.

He gathers himself in a series of ritualistic movements. It begins with a swapping of his shirt. Then baby oil on his shaved head. Next, he changes his shoes and puts on a necktie. Following his cues, I put my things into an employee storage unit made up of stacked crates. Marco shuts the door, then locks it from the inside.

"Why are you locking the door?" I protest.

"*Ay*, please. Calm your tits. I'm not going to do anything to you," he reaches into his coat pocket and takes out a one-hitter and a sandwich-sized bag of weed.

"I just want some breakfast," he smiles devilishly.

"Yessss." I celebrate, pleasantly surprised by the turn of events.

"You want some? Just a pull, though," he pauses. "I should start acting like your boss at some point."

"It's probably better if I save brain cells. I have a lot to learn today."

This rejection of the good herb is more in defense of the second half of my day than it is for this one. I would be too paranoid to exist at TLC if I get high this early in the day. The stank aroma has already attached itself to me, though. I'm pretty sure I already caught contact. A guilty by association kind of thing, if you will.

"Fair enough." he shrugs.

Watching Marco pack his bowl makes it official. I love him. Who offers you pot on the first day of work? This guy does. He holds in the smoke for a few seconds, opens a vent, and blows into it. The airflow whisks away the funky smell in seconds. My now high-ass manager sprays himself with cologne and squirts breathe freshener into his mouth.

"Time to seize the day. Let's go."

For the rest of the shift, Marco Antonio shows me how things work at Giggles. I shadow him as he juggles between the kitchen, mixing drinks at the bar, clearing tables, and teaching me the restaurant's operating system. By 2 p.m., lunch is done, and so am I. The servers are gathering at the front of the restaurant. They all begin to calculate their tips and tally receipts. I pretend not to care about having nothing to count for a job well done, as the hostess thanks patrons on their way out.

"Good job, people. Let's get those receipts in order so you can get out of here." Marco places an envelope with my name on the table. "Solei, you're done for today. Same time tomorrow?"

"You got it, boss!"

"Great, I just opened the back room. Have a good one." he blows an air kiss.

I pull thirty dollars from the envelope. Better than nothing, but silent prayers that this isn't what my tips amount to when it's official.

The back entrance helps me avoid Toni on my way

out. Finally, a moment to myself, and the first thing I think of is TLC. Anxiety ravels in the pit of my stomach. I distract myself with a book on the short ride downtown, and some chill R&B music plays in my ear as I walk into the obscure building hidden in plain sight. Mr. grouchy doorman greets me indifferently when I enter the lobby, but I still smile at him. As I wait, Cheri and Lola catwalk into the lobby.

"Hi, James." Lola flirts with the old man.

His face lights up like a schoolboy – the complete opposite of how he has interacted with me.

Femmes rule the world.

"Hello, ladies. You look so beautiful today." he beams.

Lola signs the book as Cheri walks towards the elevator, where I'm waiting.

"You're back. I thought you'd be scared off like the other girls. I'm glad you have bigger balls than that," she pouts her bottom lip. "I would've been sad."

"Really?" I question sarcastically, not believing this claim to have been so affected by my absence when she barely knows me. "And why would you be so sad?"

"We need new faces around here, that's all." her playfulness switches up.

Regret invades the space between us. I should've flirted back with her.

"Hi, welcome back!" Lola walks over just as the elevator arrives.

She leans in and kisses me on the cheek. Her perfume lingers as Cheri rolls her eyes. I pretend not to notice.

Let me find out she's jealous.

This attention gives me a confidence boost that I haven't felt in weeks.

"Have you chosen a name yet? It better be something super sexy." Lola continues.

The elevator bounces into place on the fourth floor.

"Can you help me pick one?"

"Of course. We'll come up with something good for you."

"Perfect timing, ladies. We have a client coming in an hour." Becca discloses from behind the front desk.

"Who's on the menu today?" Lola asks playfully.

"Alexander the Russian. So, hurry up and get ready."

"Ew, I can't stand him. He smells like metal, and he's a jerk," Cheri complains. "I guess I'm wearing brown lipstick today. He once told me that it makes me look too 'ethnic.' Thanks for the tip, jerk."

By the end of the sentence, she's mumbling to herself and headed to get ready.

"Well, I'm wearing my red lipstick because he loves it, and I want my Chloe shades!" Lola adds as she walks into the lounge.

Her energy stirs the room. The ladies who are already here get worked up when she walks in.

"I'm going to have you sit in the social circle, but you won't be available for a session with him." Becca is filling in today's appointments into a leather-bound pad.

"What's the social circle?"

"That's how our clients determine who they want to have a session with each time they come in. The ladies gather around him, her, or them, mingle, ask questions, then they let me know who they've chosen."

"Sounds simple enough. A few things, though. First, I still haven't come up with a name. And second, can I show you my outfit to see if you approve?"

"Yes, of course!"

"I wasn't sure what to wear. I normally don't dress girly."

Becca steps back to size up how my black and royal blue men's jacket pairs up with my baggy jeans.

"You looked way more feminine yesterday."

"I was trying to get the job," I admit.

"True. Okay, let me see what you've got. As for a name, let me think of some ideas. Candy, Diamond, Jewel, Godiva," she pauses to think of more suggestions.

"Godiva? Like the chocolate?" I tease.

"Hey, at least I have ideas."

"I have the perfect name for you!" Lola interrupts with a glass of white wine in hand. "Prophecy."

"That's it. That's the one." Becca cosigns.

"Prophecy. It has so much edge and mystery to it." I consider Lola's suggestion.

"I know. Just like you."

Oh. Hello. Are these girls flirting with me? Or are they just doing what girls do when they're extra gay with friends?

"I wish I would've thought of it for myself," Becca

concedes. "Okay, miss Prophecy, show me your outfit."

I pull out a red and black plaid skirt, a black V-neck blouse, and wedges. All borrowed from my sister's closet.

Lola laughs.

"That's cute, but it's not sexy. You might some clients with a schoolgirl or popstar fetish, but that's about it. These men want what they don't get at home, and that's seduction."

Cheri returns wearing a black corset with a diamond-shaped cut-out exposing her abs, fishnet stockings, and black stilettos. My cheeks flush. I try not to stare, but every inch of her is capturing my attention.

"What are you girls talking about?"

"We're helping Prophecy get her brand together," Becca replies.

"Prophecy? Where did that come from?"

"Lola suggested it."

"Oh, did she now? Aren't you helpful?"

She walks past us and into the lounge with an air of hostility. Lola follows her.

"What's going on with those two?"

"I think Cheri likes me and is feeling territorial," I brag.

"Is that right? What makes you so sure?"

"Because I know how girls act when they like somebody."

"All right now, I see you."

We laugh at my bold claim, before Lola returns with a weathered, slouch purse hanging off her shoulder and a look of determination.

"Come with me, please."

I follow like a puppy.

"Take this off," she orders.

A rotation of looks is pulled from the rack until she finds a leather halter top and a mini skirt to match.

My shoulders and mid-section are more exposed than I would prefer but looking in the mirror feels lovely. The six inch heels that Becca gave me are a whole other challenge. The harder I try, the more my walk resembles a linebacker – not due to a lack of femininity – they just happen to be too small. These shoes are also the only other option besides the wedges; my original choice of footwear, which, according to Lola, would be too "tacky" to stare at all day, is no longer an option.

"Wow, this is going to take some work. You're such a tomboy." she declares. "Have you ever worn heels before?"

"Of course, I have. I wore heels for two of my cousin's weddings and my Sweet Sixteen. I just need some practice."

"Well, as long as you don't walk, you look hot. And with a name like Prophecy? Done and done."

She examines me from head to toe, searching for details to fix.

"Let your hair down."

I do as she says, shaking my mop out of the loose ponytail it's tied up in.

"Your hair is so long."

A look in her eyes confirm an attraction between us. Heat flushes across my face, and a fidget throughout my body. Lola sits on top of the counter and pulls me between her legs to apply red lipstick. An ache rolls through the lower part of my extremities as our bodies border one another.

"Press your lips like this." she makes a popping sound with her mouth.

I press my lips together slowly and pucker them. Lola does the same.

"You're good to go, Prophecy. Knock 'em dead, kiddo."

A sexy linebacker in heels stares back at me when I check myself out in the mirror again.

"Here I go. Wish me luck."

Maintaining balance and being seductive at the same time requires all of my focus. It feels like Lola's watching me from behind. When I turn to ease the anxiety and prove myself wrong, I find a highly entertained Lola poking her head out of the doorway.

Becca whistles as I walk past her.

"These heels are killing me already. I need a drink."

The first thing I do is pour myself some Pinot Grigio. The chill of the wine dampens the glass on contact. Cheri comes in seconds later for a refill. I move out of the way and lean against the counter to get a better view of her body.

"So, how old are you?" she asks.

"Nineteen. How 'bout you?"

"I just turned eighteen last month."

"You look older than that."

"Gee, thanks. You sure know how to compliment a lady."

Realizing how wrong that sounds, I fumble to correct myself.

"I don't mean that as an insult at all. You just exude this womanly energy."

"You think so?" she seems pleased with my correction. "I was feeling a little fat today."

"Fat? Are you kidding me? No, your body is amazing. I wish you could see what I see."

I test the boundaries.

"Yeah? Lend me your eyes and give me a glimpse of what you see." she dares.

I study thick, high-heeled legs, the caramel in her complexion, skin patterned by the Xs of her fishnet stockings, and hips that widen just enough to bow back into the tiny circumference of her waist. The definition of abdominal muscles compliments the lingerie she's wearing. Full breasts are held together greedily by the fabric. The motion of my gaze is deliberate, slow, and steady.

"I'm ready for a drink. Let's get this day going already." Lola crashes the party.

Cheri ignores her, eyes still fixed with mine. I lose my train of thought. My attention is altered by Lola's need for a wine glass.

"Now what?" I ask.

"Now we wait," Cheri answers. "We drink, watch TV, do homework, sleep and *play games*."

LARRY

I t's been a week since I started my employment at the restaurant and TLC. Enough time to con-clude that I'm better at playing "dress up" than a waitress. For anyone who has never been a server in midtown Manhattan during a lunch crowd, here's a quick run-through:

You walk into a quiet, ghost town of a dining area. There's time to have some *cafecito*, freshen up, set your tables – and if you're lucky to have a boss like mine – there's even time for a quick toke in the employee's closet. By 11:30 a.m., you'll get a couples of tables. Under these conditions, you have time to offer the highest degree of attentiveness. Once noon rolls around, you have a few more tables seated in your area. The pace quickens. You find yourself reminded of the extra dressing they asked for the last time you came around.

There's another table that has been waiting to order, but you can't quite get to them yet in the shuffle of orders hot off the grill and drinks crowding the bartender's area waiting for delivery. The tension builds as you dash back and forth while being scrutinized by "hangry" nine-to-fivers, ready to eat the next human they see. A ticking clock closes in on their shrinking stomachs. They're seconds away from walking out and grabbing a slice of pizza instead. The only thing keeping them in their seats is the time they've already invested and the promise of food they can already taste.

When I finally have a moment to take the order of

a large table that has been giving me dirty looks, they pretend the meeting is more important than the meal, but they're ready with their orders.

"Great, I'll get these in ASAP," I assure them.

"Can I get a frozen piña colada while I wait?" a tightly wound woman demands.

The orders are in quickly.

All smiles and looks of gratitude greet me when I return with their drinks. Each one is placed in front of its respective customer. Suddenly, an imbalanced lean forward, tips the serving tray from its center of gravity. The frosted hurricane glass filled with piña colada spills over in slow motion, down one of their backs.

"Oh, my god! I'm so sorry." I hold up a wad of napkins in my defense.

The well-dressed man's face is in total shock. The creases of his wrinkles are now a contrasting red and pale white.

"ARE YOU FUCKING KIDDING ME?" he howls.

Marco, who had initially walked away from the scene laughing hysterically, has returned with hand towels and charisma in an attempt to neutralize my biggest mistake of the week.

"Hi, I'm the manager. My apologies for this mess. Solei is new here. How about I take ten percent off your tab to make up for it?" Marco's poise dominates the conversation. "Sound good, sir?"

"Okay, sure. Thank you." the man says with resignation.

He's now seated in an exaggerated posture to keep his skin from making contact with the shirt. Understanding the double-edged embarrassment, Marco caters to them for the rest of their meal. I play the sidelines and apologize one last time as they leave.

"They left you a $100 tip," he declares.

"What? No way."

"See for yourself," he holds out the signed receipt:

We've all been new at something before. Good luck!

"Well, that's yours. You did most of the work, anyway."

"*Ay*, please. I make bank here. You keep it."

"Maybe I should spill drinks on people more often," I joke. "This is my best tip so far."

"Yeah, right," he laughs. "Try that with one of these catty old hags that come in here. They'll have you for lunch."

"Thanks, by the way. I saw you take off when it happened."

"Of course, I did. I couldn't stop laughing. I needed a moment to gather myself." his hands mime an attempt at centeredness while he takes a deep breath.

We reconvene at the end of our shift to smoke again.

"You should come back for the after-work party tonight."

Marco chokes on his ganja, then passes it. The coughing gets passed along with an instant high tingling in my throat, then a rush to my head.

"I can't tonight. I'm working my other gig."

"Oh, yeah. I forgot about your other job. How's that going?"

Uncertainty anchors my words. Should I be honest? What if he switches up on me?

Marco waits for an answer.

"I mean, you don't have to tell me if you don't want to."

"You promise not to judge?"

"Honey, there's nothing you can say that I haven't seen, fucked, or heard myself. Nothing surprises me anymore."

"Okay, I work at a place that fulfills fantasies."

A puff of smoke gets hacked halfway into Marco's lungs.

"A what?"

"We entertain rich people's fantasies."

"*¡Nena!* That's scandalous. What kind of fantasies?"

"The craziest one so far was this couple that had me watch them have sex while I played with myself."

"Kinky!" Marco blurts out, "I can't believe they still have those places."

"Of course, they do. This city will forever be the land of freaks."

"And you're not scared?"

His question brings me back to an S&M session I watched Becca host yesterday. It felt like we were participating in a satanic ritual – the screams and whimpers. Recurring memories have been haunting me since.

"Some of it scares me," I admit.

"Be careful, *nena*. People that are into that kind of stuff tend to get obsessive. Their minds don't work the same. God forbid one of them gets crazy on you.

¡Ay no!" Marco makes the sign of the cross and blesses it with a kiss on his fingers. "Let's not even think like that, but if anything happens, you call me."

His protective, older brother vibe puts a smile on my face. It also invites a wave of anxiety. Everyone that has come in so far seems pretty average, even the S&M client. That doesn't make them normal, though.

What is normal?

Am I normal?

My thoughts tentacle into different scenarios and what the potential outcomes of working at TLC could lead me to. The effects of smoking are slowly inviting paranoia to the party and keeping its claws dug into my psyche. Visions of the past week feature themselves in the reel of my mind. The fact that Larry will be coming in today has now taken center stage in my mind. Becca wasn't exaggerating when she warned me about his preferences.

LARRY

I had been at the front desk with the girls yesterday when he called to confirm his session. She spoke to him first, and then we joined in on speakerphone.

"Hello, ladies! I'm coming tomorrow for an all-day session, so I want you to eat a heavy dinner tonight and lots of fluids tomorrow. I'm excited to see you all and meet the new girl."

My guard went up instantly. The feeling wasn't mutual.

"We're excited, too. See you tomorrow," Becca responded, feigning enthusiasm on our behalf.

As soon as the call ended, Brandy shook off shivers rolling down her spine.

"That man gives me the willies."

"It's the easiest money I make here. Who gets paid to use the bathroom? We do," Becca laughs. "I'm ordering Chinese food. Does anybody else want?"

Brandy gagged, hearing her words.

"That's so nasty! See, white people be into all that weird stuff. Black people don't do shit like that."

"Please don't pull the race card when it comes to kink. I'm pretty sure some crazy shit's happening in the Safaris of Africa. I bet somebody is having sex with a zebra right now," Becca countered.

The room erupted into laughter.

"Well, good luck with that. I'm taking tomorrow off." Brandy finalized.

Becca made the rest of us promise we wouldn't call out. So, today I'll be meeting the toilet slave. A rush of light-headedness floods my senses as I walk out of Giggles and to the train station. When I finally get to TLC, I've forgotten all about Larry. I'm daydreaming about Lola and Cheri instead. The reality that I have a crush on each of them for different reasons has settled in.

Cheri is more curious about the world. Her questions and conversations are more profound than those

I've had with Lola – who has a bubbly, flirty personality and shares her love of fashion, movies, and music with me. My solar plexus is in full orbit at the thought of seeing them both.

James beams as I enter the lobby. We're cool now that he's gotten to know me better. Cheri helped me understand his perspective on how it feels to see such young girls coming in and out of TLC.

"He doesn't get why we're exploiting ourselves, and he's kinda right," Cheri explained. "Imagine what anyone would *think* happens in this place and what actually does happen."

"Heeeey." Becca is hanging out with some sketchy dude at the front when I arrive.

There's something about the way she extends the word that sticks out to me. Her friend shakes my hand with wired energy that draws notice to his dilated pupils. Becca's eyes reveal the same "deer in headlights" gaze.

When Ana returns from the lounge, it allows for an escape to this energy exchange with a beeline straight to the dressing room. I'm finally coming down from the uneasiness after my conversation with Marco Antonio, and I don't want to go back into that headspace.

A knock on the door nearly gives me a heart attack. It's Becca.

"Hey, so that's one of my connects that I told you about. He has weed, Molly, X, and coke if you want anything."

"Honestly, I smoked before I came here, and I'm feeling off," I admit. "I just need a drink to calm my nerves."

"Here, have some of this." Becca pulls a baggie from her bra. "It's pure, uncut, unadulterated, high quality, Grade A white girl."

I've partaken in these extra-curricular activities before, but it's not my drug of choice. The need to snap out of this loop I'm circling is intense, though. Becca serves me a bump on the flat surface between my thumb and index finger.

"Do another on the left to keep it balanced," she encourages.

The nasal drip comes down almost immediately as I serve myself again. Becca scoops a pinky nail to shovel out a hit when I pass the baggie back.

"Oh shit, I've never noticed that before." I chuckle.

"Convenience," she winks.

"Can you get me a twenty?"

The appetite for more stimulation is activated.

"That's it? You sure? For the whole weekend?"

"I'm not going to be on this shit all weekend. That's just to help me get through this whole Larry business."

"Oh, that's why you're acting weird. I get it." Becca checks her nostrils in the mirror and smears a finger full of crystals against her teeth.

If you've never poisoned yourself with this artificial substance, you should know that this is standard practice. Spreading it across your teeth causes a numbing sensation that amplifies the high.

Everything feels different now that I'm alone again. My heart is pounding like a tribal drumbeat, but I don't feel tense anymore. It's now pure adrenaline. I'm on top of the world. Fixing my hair and makeup has suddenly become more fun. I take off my sneakers and throw on flip-flops instead. The heels can wait.

Becca places a small, yellow bag on the counter as I walk past her. I grab it casually, stuff it into my bra, and carry on. Sugar, Lola, and Angel are in the lounge.

"What's up, ladies?" I greet them with a burst that mirrors Lola's way of a grand entrance.

"It's about time. You're late today." Lola reprimands me playfully, then gets up from the dining room table.

She kisses me half on the lips, half on the cheek. Feeling bold, I return the kiss more accurately. Lola looks shocked. Did I overstep my boundaries? She basically kissed me a few seconds ago. What's the difference? Maybe she's just friendly, and I misinterpreted it. Am I being extra gay right now? I feel like crawling into myself and disappearing. The seclusion of the large sectional in the back draws me in for some invisibility.

Lola returns with drinks in hand.

"Cheers!" she taps her glass to mine.

My overthinking is put to rest when she smiles back at me.

"So, tell me. What's your deal? You're obviously into girls, right?"

Lola cozies up next to me on the couch.

"I'm very much into girls," I reply. "I'm not even sure I like guys anymore. Working here isn't helping that at all."

"Do you have a girlfriend?" she squints her eyes like she's dissecting me.

"No, my ex and I officially broke up a couple of months ago."

"Why officially? As opposed to what?"

"We were forced to break up a year ago by her mom, but we kept on seeing each other behind her back."

Camila was my first love. She attends services at a Pentecostal church on the corner of our block every Tuesday, Friday, and Sunday. Her mom is a devout Christian and preaches that homosexuality is a demon that has infiltrated one's body. I've lost count on how many times she has "rebuked me" in the name of our Lord and Savior, Jesus Christ. When she found out I was dating the youngest of her three daughters, she demanded we all stop hanging out. We didn't listen. Her sisters would sneak me in and out of their room and cover for us, but that all changed when Camila's mom allowed her to bring guys over to offset her desire of being with me. Eventually, this tactic worked, and she fell in love with one of them.

"She was only sixteen at the time, technically still a minor. Legally, I wasn't allowed to be with her."

The boyfriend part remains unsaid because it hurts too much to say out loud. Camila's guilt over going behind her mother's back, and all she had been taught about homosexuality being this malignant spirit, was enough to straighten her up.

"That's so sad. Do you still love her?"

"Yeah, I do. It sucks that it has to be this way."

The memory of this lost love breaks my heart a little bit more than it already has been. It's been getting less challenging not to think about her as much these days.

"I'll be back. I have to use the bathroom."

The goodies tucked into my top call me away from the topic at hand for a few more bumps while I pee. A combination of releasing and the drug hitting my system causes a tingling sensation at the back of my head then surges throughout my body. Happy feelings return, chasing away the clouds. There's even a creeping optimism about my failed relationship with Camila.

Lola is lying down with her headphones on when I return to the lounge. It's taken as a cue to leave her alone, so I retreat to the other couch. She seems to sense me as she opens her eyes, sits up, and fusses with her hair.

"Do you have plans tonight? I'm going out to dinner with Cheri then hitting up Exit. You should come."

"What's Exit? I've never heard of it before."

"Really? It's like the hottest club in New York right now. It's huge, the size of a warehouse, divided into different themes and music." her excitement bubbles over as she describes it to me.

"I'm down."

"Okay, perfect. We'll pick you up. Make sure you give me your number."

It's been two weeks since my last battle with Jose Cuervo – a war that I obviously lost – I'm ready to get back into the party scene, especially with how this "blow" is making me feel. I go to the front desk and write my number on a TLC business card.

"Larry should be here in twenty minutes. Please let the girls know to get pretty and shit. No pun intended. Are you ready?" she gives me a playful grin, and my stomach turns.

"Not at all."

Deep breaths and an attempt to center myself are unsuccessful. My walk is unstable as I return with the message. The heels that are part of today's look come from Lola's collection. She's given me free reign to her shoes. I put them on and brace myself while wrestling an urge to take another trip on the roller-coaster ride sticking to my side boob. I ultimately decide not to. It's better to come down for this next client.

"Ladies, Larry will be here soon. Time to get beautiful."

Lola puts the card with my phone number into the cuff of her thigh-high boots.

"Be ready by 10:30 p.m. and invite a friend, so I'm not the third wheel."

"Right. Yeah, I'll invite one of my boys."

Her request throws me for a loop. If she's the one inviting me, why would she be the third wheel? I don't want to introduce her to one of my friends. What if they like each other and I end up the matchmaker?

"No, don't bring a guy! Bring one of your lesbian friends."

Another loop.

"You think you're the only one with sapphic tendencies around here?" she continues.

"Okay, I'll bring someone," I grumble.

THE TOILET SLAVE

Larry, the toilet slave (aka the plumber), is as Becca described him. A middle-aged white man with a militant crew cut in a three-piece suit. His green duffle bag is a stark contrast to how sharp the suit fits him.

"I'm Prophecy," I break the ice.

Larry extends his hand to shake mine, and all I can think is:

This is Larry, the toilet slave, do not go in for the shake.

I grab a wineglass and hand it to him instead.

"Ah yes, the newest addition to the TLC goddesses. Here's to a productive day."

A full grin consumes his already thin lips, exposing bleach-white over yellow, denture-perfect-looking teeth. His presence causes a shudder down my spine and goosebumps on my skin. Knowing what Larry is coming here to do makes the meet-and-greet more challenging to sit through. With other clients, there's a sense of privacy when you enter the room with them. Their fetish remains secret behind the veil. This one floats sluggishly above our heads. I sense it while looking around the room at each of the girls. We all sip from our glasses in awkward synchronicity – adding to the stiffness in the air.

"All right then, I'm going to set myself up. You can start coming into the chamber in exactly fifteen minutes, and I'll be open for the next couple of hours."

The tension eases as he walks out. A fashion magazine becomes my escape from engaging too soon. Each article and quiz gets my full attention until I reach the style tips on the last pages. When I come back to the present moment, a couple of hours have passed. Another half hour comes and goes while I contemplate my next move. The other girls have been taking turns and refilling their drinks like an assembly line. Finally, I serve myself a glass and gulp it down in seconds. It's my turn to visit the chamber.

Larry is completely exposed and strapped to the wooden board on the floor. His flaccid penis greets me first. Shit. I didn't realize he'd be naked for this. Why couldn't it be some kinky leather outfit or something eccentric? Not with his awfulness out in the air. Floral aromas and burning incense from a heated potpourri dish barely masks the smell. There are baby wipes within reach on top of the sink.

On his left, a stack of fifties.

On his right, a stack of hundreds.

Inside the chair's base, looking up from the oval opening, Larry isn't the king of this throne. The feeling of absolute power makes me smile. I'm about to relieve myself onto this white man's face. I decide I want that $100 bill. As a matter of fact, I want a $100 and a $50.

Determined to get this over with, I place myself into a seated position and concentrate hard. It's tough to ignore the fact that this person is staring at my most private parts as they do their thing – and from an angle that no one has ever or will ever see again, for that matter!

My fluids gush at will.

Larry moans, arches his back, and bucks his hips forward. A violent jerk seizes him within the straps. He reaches a climax then slips into labored breathing.

Focus.

With my eyes shut now, I try to ignore the warmth of his breathing below me. My spirit detaches from the physical with an out-of-body realization of what is happening right now. An itty-bitty nugget drops from between my cheeks. It's what I can muster before deciding that's all I've got.

The baby wipes aren't as close as they first appeared, forcing me to stand up to reach them. What happens next is, by far, the most monstrous thing I've experienced in my life. I look down the gun barrel that is Larry's face staring back at me, with a piece of my waste in his mouth. My stomach churns with acidic wine. I swallow it back down.

"Don't forget to take a bill from each stack," he reminds me through an echo against the bowl.

Nausea rushes through me as I grab the money. The potpourri is now a source of resentment, and the fresh air in the hallway welcomes me back to the real world. An image of Larry's face in the toilet bowl flashes through my mind. Desperately needing a moment to gather myself, I run to the bathroom. As soon as the door closes behind me, I begin to gag.

Did I really just do that?!

All the power that surged just a few minutes ago has evaporated into nothingness. There's a knock on the door as I start to wash my face.

"Give me a sec," I try to stop my voice from cracking.

"Open up. It's Lola."

Tears start to form at the edges of my eyes. An overwhelming emotion takes over as I begin to full-on, ugly cry.

"Can you give me –" a gasp for air and normalcy cuts off my sentence.

"Open up," she demands.

There's a persistence in her voice that tells me she's not going to walk away. I regulate my breathing and let her in.

"Oh, no. What's wrong with you, babe?"

Lola cradles my face in her hands, then closes the door behind her. It's impossible to get a word past the lump in my throat.

"Hey, calm down. What happened? Did he hurt you?" she questions aggressively.

"No," I choke out, still trying to control my nerves.

"Shh, it's okay. Just breathe."

"I just —" another heave cuts off my sentence.

Lola wraps herself around me as I continue to take deep breaths. After giving me a moment, she pulls away and looks into my eyes.

"Better?"

"Yeah, sorry. That was just too much for me." I rewash my face, then lock eyes with my reflection in search of familiarity. I'm nowhere to be found.

Lola puts her arm around my torso and hugs me. Her intimacy is terrifying. A charge of energy flows between us when I turn around. Heat radiates from the core of Lola's body. Wet lips and an open mouth meet mine as our tongues collide. We gravitate closer towards each other. The world spirals as I pull away just in time to stop myself from going any deeper. My vision readjusts to see her lips puckered and eyes still closed. She slowly opens them and smiles at me.

"We should get back out there," I whisper.

"Yes, we should." Lola fixes her skirt.

I step out into the hallway, still emotional but feeling higher than any drug could ever take me.

DOUBLE DATE

The first person that comes to mind for to-night's festivities is my best friend, of course. Sammy's entertaining as hell, the only one I can trust to bring along on this covert operation, and she'll help me figure out whether to pursue Cheri or Lola. We haven't spoken since that crazy night at Krash, though. Hopefully, she doesn't already have plans.

Sammy picks up after a few rings.

"Finally! I've been calling you for weeks now. Where have you been?"

"What are you even saying? No, you haven't."

"I've been calling your house mad times a day. I was worried about you." her tone changes to genuine concern.

"Dude, I lost my phone that night. What the hell happened to us?"

"Yo, we were so far gone. Do you remember anything at all?"

Sammy's question has a hint of something more – like there's a secret she's about to share.

"Nothing after those tequila shots."

"I told you to lay off that shit. I was chillin' with my Bacardi and orange juice, like a true Puerto Rican." she declares. "So, tell me this. Do you remember what happened with the twins?"

"What twins? Natalia and Valentina? Oh shit, tell me what happened!"

The twins are these Dominican sisters that we've been obsessing over for months now. A faint image of them walking into the club flashes back into my memory.

"Yes, those twins. Yo, we had sex with them in the same room!"

"You're lying." I challenge.

"I swear to God I'm not. We were like porn stars up in there just giving it to them." Sammy is boasting in full-on character mode, giving all the juicy details I didn't know I needed.

"Valentina was screaming your name like a beast, and I still have scratches and bite marks from Natalia. I can't believe you don't remember that."

"Do you know how bad I've wanted to get with Valentina? To finally hook up and not even remember. Damn you, José Cuervo."

"Sucks to be you. I remember everything," she teases. "Anyway, they want to see us. What time can you be ready?"

"Nah, that's why I'm calling you. We already have

plans tonight with these two sexy girls from my job. Tell them we'll link up another day."

It's no contest on who we should hang out with. The twins are boring compared to Cheri and Lola.

"What? Who?" Her excitement turns to sheer giddiness. "You're the bestest friend a little lesbian could have."

Suddenly, a call comes in on the other line. It's an unknown number. I think it's Lola.

"Hold on, don't hang up."

I try to sound nonchalant when I click over, "Hey, what's up?"

"Wow, you sound different on the phone. Ever thought about doing phone sex with that voice?" Lola flirts on the other end of the line.

"Oh, yeah? Tell me what you're wearing?" I take the opportunity and run with it.

"I don't mean right now, silly." Lola giggles.

She's calling for my address. I keep the call brief, then click back to Sammy.

"I thought you forgot about me," she says.

"Sorry, that was one of the girls. Be at my place by 10 p.m. We can pre-game, and I'll catch you up on all the wild shit I've been doing. Oh, and dress extra fly tonight."

I have enough time for a quick nap before I start getting ready. By the time Sammy rings the bell, I've set up a small nook in the backyard for us to chill. There are little snow patches that came down a few days ago, but there's a fall crisp in the air that's warm enough to smoke inconspicuously without getting caught.

Sammy hugs me like she hasn't seen me in years.

"You don't know how glad I am to see that you're okay," she says, still hugging me. "I'm guessing you also don't remember telling Valentina you were going to use the bathroom and never coming back?"

"Seriously?"

Sammy recounts more details from that night, piecing it together for me. Apparently, I stumbled by their father and thanked him for having such beautiful daughters. Whatever else I said to him must've been somewhat coherent because he's been asking Valentina about me since.

"Wow, I don't remember any of that," I admit.

"I only have memories of my mother yelling at me."

"Yeah, I heard it from her, too. She cursed me out when I called the next day."

All of my friends have gotten a mouthful from her at least a few times. My mother tells everyone off at some point. It's not because she thinks I'm this perfect kid, and they influence me to do wrong. Mami knows the truth; I'm trouble, and my friends are my accomplices.

"I've never been that blacked out before." I contemplate.

"Well, you're safe. That's all that matters."

"True that."

We clink our drinks in celebration, then details of our latest adventures are laid out on the table for each other. The first thing on the list of tells is my latest line of work, which leads to the new ladies in my life.

"I'm here thinking you're behaving yourself, and you're out there being the king of kink." she jokes. "So, what is this place?"

"It's roleplay and fantasy."

I wait for a reaction while Sammy stares at me blankly.

"What the hell does that mean? Are you playing some Dungeons & Dragons shit now?"

"It's this whole other world, where we fulfill people's deep, dark fantasies."

"Fulfill fantasies? Like what?"

"Lower your voice."

It's no secret that the wind carries whispers spoken in confidence. My mother, Yolanda De La Vega Romero, is the biggest bruja of them all. She somehow discovers things unseen with no idea of how the knowledge comes to her.

"They come in to get whipped, stepped on, watch us do things, and get spit on... all types of crazy shit."

"You're nuts. Only you would do something like this, I swear. Do you have sex with them?"

"Damn, you think I would be taking it that far? We're doing crazy things, but not *alla* that."

Sammy's at a loss for words. I can see her gears going as she processes the gossip. Maybe I shouldn't have told her anything. Is she going to think I'm having sex for money now?

"Okay, who are these two girls we're meeting up with?" she jumps off-topic.

"Oh, yeah... Lola and Cheri."

"Are those their stripper names?"

"Kind of." I laugh.

Had I known their real names, we'd be having a different conversation. Every detail I've observed gets shared with Sammy like we're kids at the playground.

"Here's the thing. I like them both, but I like Lola more."

"What the hell? I thought this was a double date," Sammy complains.

"It is. I'm just confused about who I'm supposed to be on a date with. I think it's Cheri."

"So, I'm a fourth wheel to your threesome."

"How about this? Let's just go with the flow and see who vibes with who. If you see Lola getting friendly with me, then entertain Cheri. And vice-versa, I think. Just pay attention to how Lola is acting."

"You're lucky I love you. I can only agree to this because I know you have good taste in women, and it'll be worth it."

Sammy pulls up the collar of her shirt, feeling good about the game plan.

My phone vibrates.

"They're about to pull up."

Sammy watches as I take out the yellow baggie that Becca hooked me up with.

"Want some?"

"Who are you? And what did you do to my best friend?" she teases.

"This is the newest version of the old me. No more heartbreak for this kid," I declare, thinking of my breakup with Camila.

On our way out, I call down to Papi, who is working on a project in the basement. His artwork is all over our home, from wood carvings, garden pieces, and painted arches with Roman columns in our living room. Papi, Kelvin Romero, Sr., is the South Bronx

Picasso.

"Daddy, I'm heading out. Love you."

"Okay, *muñeca*. I love you. Be careful." he shouts back up.

Lola steps out of the passenger side of a black four door. Sammy reaches out her hand with the charm set on high.

"You're even more beautiful than Solei said. This is going to be an interesting night."

"Sammy, this is Lola." I shake my head slightly, enough for her to be the only one that catches it.

"Lola is only for TLC. In the real world, I go by Adelina." she winks at me, then turns back to Sammy. "You better be a fun date. Come on, I'm sitting in the back with you."

Sammy shrugs and gives me a confused look, then motions for Lola to go in before her.

Adelina.

I repeat her name in my mind. That's a name that could roll off my tongue in the middle of the night. No more calling her Lola.

Cheri is in the driver's seat, beaming her wide, infectious smile.

"Sammy, this is Jesenia." Adelina follows up.

Hearing their real names makes me feel like we're meeting for the first time.

"Where to first?" I ask.

Jesenia turns to me with a raised eyebrow.

"You're not in charge tonight, sugar tits. I am."

The conversations flow so effortlessly that it's like we've known each other for years by the time we get to the city. Our first stop is dinner at a speakeasy in the Flatiron District called C'est La Nuit. There are candlelit settings for ambiance and a DJ spinning electronic dance music. The crowd is full of smug Europeans speaking too loudly. Aware of my surroundings, I lengthen my spine and chuck my chin up a little higher. Spaces like this always make me feel like an outsider, but the extra effort it takes to feel like I belong is worth it.

Jesenia puts her hand on my leg and sits closer for more privacy. She tells me of a dream, one where I made an appearance. Her voice drops to a whisper for the steamiest parts. I listen intently to details of bodies intertwined, legs coiled rapturously, and how we reached a climax in the same breath.

"The best dream I've had in a while," she bites her lower lip.

This imagery leaves me bewitched with a warm tingle in my chest that flows down between my legs. The waiter refills our drinks, infiltrating the invisible curtain around us.

"Are you okay over there? It looks like you're about to have each other for dinner." Adelina says with a tinge of jealousy in her voice.

I take a deep breath and gather myself. The night's magic has officially seized effect, bringing with it lowered defenses to Jesenia's magnetism and Adelina's deep gaze. There's a disappointment in her that I can't bear. It forces me to turn my attention to the tapas that have been served, as the surge of desire for Jesenia abruptly evaporates.

Sammy changes the mood with a joke. Seeing it as a window of opportunity, I excuse myself to the bathroom. She follows.

"Dude, you're on your own here. I'm just the chaperone at this point," she complains. "I should've kept my plans with Natalia. Adelina asked me all these questions about you while you were over there, having your lust fest."

"Yo, Jesenia was telling me about the wildest dream. She had me stuck on stupid."

"I saw. You just looked horny to me." Sammy cracks.

"Horny?" I suck my teeth. "I'm not horny."

"Call it what you want. It's still that. Adelina was all up in it, trying so hard to read lips."

"I don't understand. She's the one pushing me to get to know Jesenia."

"She's testing you. Hello, this is what girls do. Adelina wants you to decide you like her enough to stop flirting with her friend. Duh."

Sammy's ability to decipher this for me is why she's my confidant. We return to find the girls red from laughing so hard. It takes some time for them to recover their breathing.

"What's so funny? I wanna to laugh, too." Sammy probes.

Adelina shakes her head.

"Nothing you would understand. It's girl talk."

"Hey, I'm still a girl under these clothes. Thank you very much," she responds.

"*Girly* girl talk. You don't count. You're like a boy-girl." Adelina points to her stilettos. "See these heels? You would need a pair to get the joke. Got it? Good."

Her rude response throws Sammy off.

"Whatever," I interject. "We don't want to be girly anyway. See these shoes?" I point down to my *hella* comfortable Vans. "They never hurt. We can go all night."

"That's hot. The way you're defending your friend like that," she gets up and grabs her purse. "Let's get out of here. We already paid the bill."

Sammy and I have never been on dates where we weren't expected to cover the check. In the lesbian community, if you are the less feminine one, there's an unspoken rule that you pay.

When we get to Exit, the line is halfway around the block. Sammy objects to wait that long to get into the club.

"Do we look like we wait on lines?" Adelina walks ahead of everyone waiting, and gives each of the bouncers a kiss on the cheek.

"Looks like it's going to get crazy tonight," she says to one of them.

"It will be, but no one is looking as good as you, baby."

The muscle head on the right leans in to kiss her on the mouth, but Adelina turns her head just in time.

"Bruno, how many times do I have to tell you I'm not interested in you like that. You're like a brother to me."

"I'm sorry. The thing is, I'm not your brother, and you're a baddie."

His associate – a chunky black dude – puts in his bid.

"Well, I'm not your brother. How about you let me tap that."

"Ew, shut up. Don't talk to me like that in front of my girlfriend." Adelina reaches out her hand for me to grab it.

I play along.

"You're a carpet-muncher? No fucking way."

"Hey man, don't talk to her like that." Bruno gets serious. "What's up, girlfriend?"

I strain to make my grip stronger when we shake hands.

"If my little sis likes you, then you're good in my book. Welcome to Exit." Bruno unhooks the velvet rope and ushers us in.

The music pulsates off the walls and floor beneath us. My first objective is to go to the bathroom. Hitting the stalls is the perfect reset button when you walk into a high-energy spot like this.

Jesenia tails me.

"I want to ask you something," she blocks me right before I go in. "Do you like Adelina or me? Be honest."

I know that this answer will change everything. No longer will it be a "cake and eat it, too" game.

"I like you both… but I know that's not right, so I

won't pursue either of you."

"That doesn't make any sense," Jesenia responds. "I know she likes you. And I think you would make a cute couple."

"We would too, though." I flirt.

"The one girl that I like, and she likes you, too! Ain't that some shit." she continues. "No, but seriously, I love that bitch. You should go for it."

Jesenia's co-sign brings with it an unburdening. I was playing with fire, and she just extinguished it for me. I've learned that when you can't make a decision, the world makes it for you, and you're lucky if you come out with anything at the end.

"I'll just have to find another lesbian to eat me out, I mean, turn me out." Jesenia jokes while letting me into the bathroom.

They're all waiting at the bar with drinks when I return.

"Cheers!" we roar.

The hours drift while dancing our asses off. The more alcohol we consume, the more affection I get from Adelina.

"You better not hurt my best friend, or I'll cut your tits off." Jesenia threatens in complete inebriation.

Little do I know, my breasts are in more danger than I could ever imagine.

MONDAY BLUES

Mami isn't too happy when I ask to borrow twenty dollars to get to work on Monday morning. A weekend of nonstop partying and shopping has left me completely broke. She gives me ten instead. The lunch shift at Giggles is a drag. By the time I get to TLC, I'm ready for a nap.

"Our next client won't be in for another two hours," Becca informs me.

Perfect. The cold weather's chill factor seeps

through the window cracks in opposition to the bare minimum heat the building provides – a good enough reason to stay in my regular clothes. I fall into a deep sleep using my coat as a blanket.

The room is darker when I wake up. Someone has adjusted the lighting to a softer setting. Lenny Kravitz strums his guitar strings out of the speakers bouncing the acoustics. His raspy vocals purify the air as he romances the object of his affections. An unrecognizable calm saturates the air.

I get up to investigate the silence, and find there's no one at the front desk. Each room is empty. My anxiety, now a rising sea, floods my mind as I reach the end of the hallway and find Becca, Angel, Lola, and Cheri in the last room. They're all over each other. Becca's face is between Angel's legs. Angel's fingers are inside of Cheri, and Lola is kissing her breasts.

The shock renders me an outsider – a voyeur on

the outskirts of all the action. Lola looks over, aware of my presence, before actually seeing me there. Within seconds she's kissing me deeply. My mouth overflows with her saliva.

It's too much.

I'm choking on something.

I pull away, gasping for air. There's blood all over her mouth, my blood. It's everywhere now, gushing out of me.

Lola doesn't flinch.

She stands there, panting like a savage beast. The heaving turns into a maniacal laugh.

"What's wrong?" she growls.

I jump out of the nightmare. My coat is still sheltering me on the couch. Angel, Brandy, and Betty are watching daytime television. The lines between sleep and awake still have me disoriented. The dream replays in my mind; Lola's face smeared with my blood, her crazy laugh, and the rumble in her voice spooks me.

It was just a dream.

It's time to freshen up and get dressed for this client coming in. I'm ready to spice things up with a new outfit that I purchased over the weekend. The look is finalized with a matte red lipstick to increase my odds of getting booked. This need to make more cash forces the realization that TLC is changing me. I've never felt like I *needed* money before.

"Wow, you look fierce." Becca whistles like a construction worker.

"Thanks, I added to my seductress wardrobe of three whole looks." I joke.

"Let me take a picture of you."

Becca pulls out an instant camera that she uses for new clients. I standby, hoping it has run out of film. Photos are not my favorite thing, especially dressed the way I am right now.

"Well, aren't you going to pose? Do something sexy."

"How does someone do sexy? That doesn't make sense. Just take the picture."

"Fine." Becca positions herself. "Can you at least pucker your lips for me?"

I arch my back, bend my knees, and purse my lips together. Chest out.

"Better?"

She catches the snapshot as it slides out of the opening.

"That lipstick is so fire on you."

The image in the photo looks nothing like me. My hair – usually tied up or in a bun – is teased into high volume. I'm wearing Lola's stilettos again. They no longer make me walk like a football player. A shimmery corset compresses my ribcage and boosts my cleavage, with black shorts that fit like panties.

"Where are the rest of the girls?"

"Well, Sugar quit because she got a job as a dog walker. Lola and Cheri said they have a school thing, and Ana is sick."

Damn, I was looking forward to seeing the girls today. The last time I spoke to them was Saturday morning as we all left the diner.

"That sucks."

"Yeah, I know. It's way too calm here today. At least The Wolf is coming in. He'll shake things up.

"Who is that?"

"He's our youngest client. The finest one, too." Becca gushes. "Late twenties, CEO of some big company. Latin. I don't know from where exactly, but his accent gives it away. He talks like he's from a Spanish soap opera. And did I mention how fine he is?"

Thank God. The last thing I need is some old man wanting me to play with his smelly beard.

With nothing better to do, I drink to combat the bitter cold around us. Angel starts a game of spades. As we play, Betty tells us stories about her time in the military and how she still has nightmares from time served in the Middle East.

"I only signed up because I wanted to get the hell out of Sweet Water, Alabama," she says with a twang I notice for the first time. "I hate that place. Let me tell you something. Cow-tipping shouldn't be the highlight of anyone's weekend."

"How did you end up in New York?" Brandy asks.

"The same reason anyone moves here, to feel alive." Betty then charges it to love – speaking about her boyfriend in reverence. "He saved me from a life of mediocrity."

I hold my wine up for a toast.

"You're an American treasure. You escaped your hometown, survived a war, followed your heart to New York, and ended up here with some badass babes. I'd say you found the adventure you were looking for."

"Here's to Sweet Water, Alabama! For sucking so much, you had to leave." Angel shouts.

We laugh and raise our glasses to her again.

The five minute warning bell sounds off. I have now consumed too many glasses of White Zinfandel, and a spirit of sexy is racing through my body. The costume I'm wearing is also stirring this confidence. I ask Brandy to help me reapply my lipstick. Our shared body heat ignites a running fever I have imbibed myself into.

"Your lips look so kissable with this lipstick," she says.

Her words fuel the current between us.

Each one of the girls makes their way to a seat within the social circle. The client enters while we're patiently waiting for him. Freshly touched up perfume, heels adjusted, and another glass of wine for good measure. The liquid courage commissions a provocative side as I cross my legs. He pays attention. Becca was right; this guy is ridiculously good-looking. It makes me wonder what his sins are. I'm sure he doesn't have a hard time attracting women.

Maybe he's a serial killer.

No, no, no. I can't think like this. How am I supposed to book this session if I'm sitting here thinking he's a murderer?

The girls take their turns talking to the client. I say nothing and wait for him to address me first. His eyes follow as I flip my hair over. Angel is going in about her fascination with fire and basically outing herself as a pyromaniac. Somewhere between wondering if this guy is Dexter and reminding myself to be seductive, I lost a handle on the conversation.

"Are you Prophecy?" he finally directs his attention my way.

"Oh, so you've heard of me?"

"Yeah, I've heard some things," he teases. "From Andy, mostly."

"Well, he's not a reliable source." I counter. "He just wants you to spend your money here."

His eyes follow as I uncross my legs.

Wait, what am I doing? The conversation where Becca lets me know what his fetish or fantasy is didn't happen. What if it's too much for me?

The game of seduction stops.

Angel and Brandy keep talking, but I'm unable to adjust to their words – the alcohol has officially taken over. The kitchen becomes my sanctuary until he walks out of the lounge. A decision has been made.

Dear God, please don't let it be me.

Another nap would be amazing. I'm also really not in the mood to be coy and put on airs while pretending to be a lady. Becca walks in.

"Prophecy, you're up."

"You didn't even tell me what he likes. What am I in for?"

"There will be a bag of grapefruits. It's usually a dozen or so. You take each one and throw it at him as hard as you can. Compliment his body. Tell him how strong he is for withstanding such pain. You get extra tips for that." Becca squares up.

"So, I just hit him anywhere?"

"Yup. Then he'll offer you another fifty for a massage. Do it." she advises.

"I'm so tipsy. There's a good chance I'll miss him completely. Does he give extra for that, too?"

Becca yanks my arm and pulls me out of the kitchen.

"Go. Time starts now." she pushes me towards the rooms. "It's a one hour block. I'll knock at forty-five minutes then on the hour, if you're not out yet."

I've only done thirty-minute sessions so far. Maybe getting drunk wasn't a bad idea, after all.

The Wolf faces me when I enter. He's already down to his boxers and black socks with an athletic, chiseled body. Making him feel worshipped will be easy. The grapefruits are stacked on the dentist-looking chair.

"Was this explained to you?" he begins, exuding dominance.

"Yes, but I should warn you that I played softball in high school."

He smiles, pleased with my answer.

"Have a seat."

The Wolf begins with questions about my personal life. Each answer I provide is made up on the spot. I can be whoever I want – why not make it fun? The topic then changes to his stresses and responsibilities of running a business.

"My biggest fear is not succeeding," he admits. "It haunts me every night. I have over 15,000 employees that I'm responsible for."

Something in the distance of his mind distracts him.

"There are days I just want to run away from it all,

but then I would feel guilty about giving up. The hamster wheel goes on and on."

The Wolf finishes his drink and serves another. My glass is still full; the need to pace myself feels more urgent now. Hesitant of what to say, I massage his shoulders. This part is supposed to happen after the grapefruits, but I'm acting on instinct. His upper body relaxes from my touch.

"Then, I come here and do this thing. I feel so good when I'm here. My wife and I haven't had sex in almost a year. This is the most intimate contact I get."

The weight of his load is exhaled with a deep sigh. His shoulders slump. A comfortable silence dwells between us. I massage his scalp and pull on his hair in a soft tug. My fingertips press each temple in a circular motion. The Wolf pulls away and buries his face into both palms. Seconds later, I realize he's crying.

"Are you okay? Do you want to stop the session?"

"No, it's fine. I'll still pay you extra," he assures.

I'm more concerned with having to coddle him as he wipes the tears away.

"I caught my wife having sex with another man yesterday. They were so into it that they didn't notice me standing at the door. That man was having her on my bed."

My mind wanders off to the last time I saw a man cry like this. It was Papi when he finally saw me after two months of being a runaway. My older brother, Kelvin Jr., chased me into a store I ran into for refuge. Once I saw his turquoise 1991 Camaro pull up, I knew it was the end of my freedom. He dragged me home to face my parents, and my father broke down.

"I left without them noticing and came back hours later. My wife was cold and distant, as usual." he continues.

"Why don't you tell her that you saw them?"

The Wolf's body tenses up again.

"If I tell her, then I have to leave her. What kind of man would I be if I stayed?"

"You don't have to leave her. People forgive their partners for cheating all the time."

"For respect. If I allow her to disrespect me, how will I respect myself?" he shifts to aggression. "We've been together since we were fifteen years old. I can't believe she would do this in the home I bought her."

He stands up suddenly. The tears are gone, and his breathing is heavy now. One fist punches into the other.

"She's lucky I didn't bash their fucking heads in!" his jaw is clenched as he paces back and forth.

"Maybe you should let me calm you down."

I conceal the fear he's triggering in me. If this runaway train isn't stopped now, he could get violent and take his anger out on me. The pacing continues until he finally regains control, then returns to the loveseat.

"Why don't we stop talking about her for now?

Isn't that why you came here? To escape?" I whisper in his ear. "Why don't we get on with this?"

Hands run up my thighs and around my waist as I stand before him. My fingernails claw the surface of his back and along his ribcage. He faces the wall. This is a cue. It's time for the grapefruits.

"Your legs look so strong."

I cast the first one – it hits his left leg. The Wolf's knee buckles from the impact, but he composes himself, takes a deep breath, and straightens his posture.

"THANK YOU! MAY I HAVE ANOTHER?" he cries out.

"May you have another? You are as strong as you look." I pretend to be impressed.

The next one hits his right shoulder.

"THANK YOU! MAY I HAVE ANOTHER?" he cries out.

"I wish I had a man as strong as you in my life."

The third grapefruit pelts his lower back. His breathing intensifies.

"Turn around."

The Wolf obeys. His muscles contract and tighten from the pressure of his panting. A sudden locking of eyes takes me out of character, and the intensity of his gaze overwhelms me.

Another grapefruit.

This one strikes him on the stomach; abdominal muscles stiffen as it ricochets.

"Come here," he says.

I pause, then surrender to his will.

The Wolf targets a kiss on my lips, but I dodge it swiftly.

"I don't kiss on the mouth," I recall this line from *Pretty Woman* and use it to my advantage.

The kisses land on my neck instead. A part of me is giving in; the other part is scared of what I'm allowing to unfold. The world spins around my head. A surreal feeling takes over as soft rock music plays from the speakers, and he kneels before me to remove my shoes – first my left, then my right. I position myself on the sofa as The Wolf takes my toes into his mouth, tongue slithering between them. An unfamiliar sensation moves through my entire being. The sucking and nibbling cause my body to shudder as I sink into the leather couch.

The Wolf's tongue makes its way up my thigh, hands following, as he kisses through the fibers of my shorts, then reaches the source of my lustfulness. His hand comes up to unbutton them. I stop him, shaking my head no, but my resistance is a half-staffed white flag.

"I just want to taste you," he whispers, reaching for my shorts again.

This time, I allow it. They come off in one quick motion. The Wolf's mouth grazes the inner part of my leg. At the same time, hands grip my hips and pull me forward. The intensity shoots chills to every inch of my frame. He licks me just once, then looks up and smiles.

I don't smile back.

A pool of mixed emotions hampers the indulgence. The Wolf puts his mouth on me again. This time the pleasure hypnotizes me as his tongue strokes the folds of my femininity. I'm dangerously close to climaxing as I suppress the moans and a desire to thrust into his face. If the girls hear me, they might get the wrong idea. Or precisely the right idea.

A knock on the door makes me jump; he doesn't react.

"Fifteen minutes left," Becca announces.

"Okay, thanks," I respond, melting into the swirling motions between my legs.

Within minutes I'm grinding, shoving his face into me, and shaking off the pleasure. The Wolf looks up. I squeeze his head with my legs, getting every last shiver before setting him free from my grip.

This time I'm the one smiling.

He starts to put his suit back on as embarrassment reddens my cheeks; I can feel the heat rising. I put my panties and shorts back on and sit there, confused about what just happened. The Wolf avoids eye contact as he puts his tie and blazer on.

"That was interesting," I say in a feeble attempt to dispel the awkwardness.

"Yeah, it was." he nods, pulls his wallet out, sets two hundred-dollar bills near the wine bucket, then walks out.

GETAWAY

Marco has let me pick up extra shifts after hearing about the last encounter at TLC. My biggest sins of smoking too much and binging on hot wings and fries are trivial compared to life in the underground. These last couple of weeks have exposed me to more life-altering moments than I've experienced in my nineteen years on this planet. A sensory overload between the girls and our clients took me for a ride on an emotional roller coaster at 180 mph with no seat belt.

The incident with The Wolf was icing on an already spoiled cake. A dark cloud binds me to the memory of him placing money on the table after eating me out. A pill too hard to swallow; a glitch-in-the-Matrix kind of mindfuck. It enforces the realization that I've been selling more than my time at TLC. Women and girls are being murdered daily for this shit. We've all read the stories of forced labor and human trafficking, and here I am signing up for it to buy expensive clothes, eat at fancy places, and party the night away. The foolishness antagonizes me.

When Sammy invites me to Philly for the weekend, I jump at the chance to escape. Leaving the city on the Cross Bronx Expressway feels like salvation. She talks the entire ride, but my inability to follow the rambling is no deterrent to her word vomit.

"I know she loves me. She's just afraid I'm going to cheat. But yo, I swear I would drop everybody if she was my girl."

Sammy doesn't come up for air once.

I wonder what Adelina is doing. We haven't spoken all week. I'm also thinking of telling Sammy about The Wolf. My only hesitation is how she'll take it. It could ruin our trip and friendship if she judges me because I've been on edge these days. Self-criticism weighs more than any cross the world can erect in your honor. This shame that has built a home in me is enough of a burden.

The decision to keep it secret becomes firm. It's my body, and I'm the only one I need to answer to. The short film playing out in my mind stages a mini "letting go" ritual. I forgive myself then release it to the wind with a promise that I'm going to enjoy this weekend.

We arrive at our destination a little after midnight. The house is full of life as Sammy's family celebrates. Marc Anthony wails romantic lines over congas, bongos, a horn section, and perfectly synced backup singers harmonizing our love of love. Sammy's uncle, Ray, woos his wife with the lyrics and a shot of Bacardi as I follow my nose to the smell of *pasteles* in the kitchen.

Giselle, Sammy's older sister, flirts with me while serving a plate of food. She always does this, and it leads nowhere.

"You're all bark and no bite."

"No, I'm not. You just haven't gotten me drunk enough," she says in between sips of *coquito*.

I wake up to her sleeping on my chest the following day, with Sammy knocked out on the couch across from us. A break of sunlight warms my face despite the frigid temperature outside. The legendary Philadelphia street art gets us out of the house early. My favorite thing to do is get lost in this city with my best friend.

"Sammy, I need a favor from you."

"Depends on what it is. Your bright ideas aren't always that bright." she teases.

"I want you to cut my hair in the same style you do

for your brothers."

Her brothers Edwin and Albert have similar buzz cuts with a tape-up in the back.

"Where's this coming from?"

"I need to switch it up. I read somewhere that every time a person cuts their hair off, it liberates them from the past. All that energetic junk they have accumulated gets cut off, too."

Sammy cracks on me, "You talk like such a hippie. I can tell you spent all your summers around *wypipo*."

"Man, shut up. Are you going to do it or not?"

"Of course, but how short are you trying to go?"

"Short, short. Like G.I. Jane, peach fuzz short. I've always wanted to cut my hair like that."

I'm now in a complete daydream about the new look. The rest of our plans get canceled in search of scissors and clippers to get the job done. Sammy's aunt, Tia Josefina, is in the kitchen cooking up another mouth-watering meal for everybody.

"Tia, can I cut Sol's hair in the bathroom? I'll sweep up when we finish." Sammy promises.

"You're cutting your hair? Why would you do such a thing?" Tia Josefina looks at me on the verge of tears.

For a young girl to chop long, beautiful hair into a boyish cut is a severe cultural offense for Latinos. I'm going to get drawn out lectures over this decision, but I have to go through with it. It's a spiritual deed at this point – like I'm absolving myself of my sins. I'm the priest and the confessional, and this is an act of penance.

"It's hair. It'll grow back." I smile.

My ponytail stays up for the first snip while Sammy tries a couple of times to shred through it all. The clipped strands are presented as a prize when she's done.

Tia Josefina plants the idea of donating it to Locks of Love. This heightens the symbolism and purpose for me. Sammy keeps trimming it down until it's time to switch over to the clippers. The hum of the machine passing over every inch of my scalp causes a flutter in my stomach. She then shapes up my hairline and cleans the edges as a finishing touch.

"I think I went too short," Sammy hesitates.

"Well, it's too late now. How does it look?"

I can easily stand up and see for myself, but I'm glued to the chair – absolutely not ready to look in the mirror yet.

"You look like a boy," Tia Josefina says, shaking her head.

I take a deep breath and decide to face myself. The precision of Sammy's lines and fading match that of professionals. Her skills have gotten better with her brother's help. Albert works at a barbershop on Prospect Ave. and has taught her all his techniques and styling.

"Yo, you hooked it up!"

I study the cut from different angles. The way she

has shaped my sideburns kind of does make me look like a boy. I caress the extra-sensitive hair follicles on my scalp in disbelief.

"Holy shit, you shaved it all off."

"I laced you up, kid." Sammy brags. "This is gonna get you so many girls."

"Do I look too much like a dude, though? My mother is going to lose her shit."

"Only the hair is like a boy. Your face is too pretty." Tia Josefina says.

It will take some getting used to, but I don't regret it one bit. A sense of relief has declared emancipation over me. After dinner, we decide to head back to New York earlier than planned. Sammy wants to see Natalia after admitting that they're madly in love. My heart drops when we pull up to the front of the house hours later. I can see Mami washing dishes through the window.

"Wish me luck."

I climb out of the backseat. Their beat-up hooptie pulls off, leaving me to deal with the obstacle ahead. Sammy – which also happens to be the name of my mother's demonic chihuahua, also known as the Son of Sam, because he's an evil little creature – barks at me when I come in. His tiny body is lunging towards my foot in full attack mode. Mami follows his lead and charges at me with a large soup spoon. Neither of them recognizing who I am.

"Ma, it's me!" I yell while keeping her arms from swinging this makeshift weapon at my head.

"I know it's you!" she fights. "What did you do to your hair?" Her arm still waving the spoon at me.

Knowing how violent Mami can be when she's angry, I keep a firm grip on her.

"Ma, calm down. You can't hit me. I'm not a kid anymore, and I'm stronger than you."

The fact that she feels justified in hitting me for

cutting my hair annoys me.

"Are you threatening me? Are you going to hit me? Go ahead, hit me." Mami dares.

She never backs down from anything she feels right about, which is pretty much everything.

"I'm not threatening you, ma. I don't want to fight. Please, just talk to me like I'm a human being." My voice softens.

Hopefully, the olive branch will calm her down. There's no need for all this drama. I have the right to do whatever I want with my hair.

"Solei, why did you do this to your hair? *Ahora te pareces como un macho*," she yells. "Is that what you want? To look like a boy?"

"There are plenty of women that cut their hair and aren't trying to look like a man. Remember Demi Moore in *Ghost*? You love her in that movie."

"Yes, but they don't have these lines. That's not the

shape of your hair."

Mami presses her index finger into the hairline along my forehead.

"That's the style. You're just overthinking it. This is like when Zuli used a razor to do lines on her head in the 80s. That was the style, right?"

Zuli is my older cousin. She's the oldest of all the cousins in my family. Knowing that she can do no wrong in my mother's eyes, I always use her as a reference when defending my actions.

Mami walks away on a rampage.

"Did you see what your daughter did?" she stomps into the living room.

Her frustrations will now spill on to Papi, who is watching TV in his favorite chair. I walk in behind her, bracing for his disappointment. Papi's opinion matters most to me. My father's eyes widen, and his mouth drops.

"*Mi muñeca*, what happened? I have to call you

muñeco now," he jokes.

"It's your fault for wanting a son when Mami was pregnant with me." I crack back.

"This is not funny," Mami interjects. "What are we going to do?"

"Do? What is there to do? She cut her hair. It'll grow back."

"And I'm an adult now. You can't tell me what to do anymore."

"I don't care if you're forty! My house, my rules." Mami yells. "You got it out of your system. Now you grow it back."

"After I enjoy it for a while. I'm not growing it back right away. So, get used to it."

She grills me a little longer, then pounds up the stairs, mumbling under her breath. Papi is now shaking his head.

"What made you do such a crazy thing?"

"I just felt the urge to chop it all off, so I did."

"You're growing it back, right?"

"Eventually." I smile.

The conversation ends there. Papi isn't the type to push a topic further than it needs to go. In the good cop/bad cop parental scenario, he's always the good cop. We watch a documentary about aliens for a bit before I retreat to my room. The privacy brings with it thoughts of Adelina. A dose of courage influences me to call her.

"Hey, stranger. Where have you been? TLC is so boring without you there."

"I'm on a mental health break. That place gets me into trouble."

"Well, I've been getting into a lot of it. You may want to come back and save me from myself."

"I have a surprise for you." I change the topic, not wanting to know what she means by that.

"I love surprises. What is it?"

"It's not a present or anything. Just a change from

the last time we saw each other."

"Did you cut your hair?"

"Damn, how'd you know?" I'm shocked by her accuracy.

"You said it's a change from the last time. It's not that hard to figure out."

"I guess I could've played that better." I laugh. "Well yeah, I cut it."

"I want to see it!" Adelina demands.

"You will. I'm coming back on Monday."

"Monday?" she protests. "I haven't seen you in a whole week. Monday is way too far. What are you doing tonight?"

"I was planning on staying in."

"Come over. I want to see you."

Adelina manages to convince me to take three trains into Queens for another late-night tryst that I'm willing to sacrifice sleep for. Add to that a twenty-minute walk from the station through the residential streets of Forest Hills. The directions bring me to the front of her house. As instructed, I follow the walkway under her bedroom window. It's lit by dancing images of late-night television. The blue glow of my cellphone screen serves as a flashlight in the dark. I send a brief text because I'm nervous:

I'm here.

A few minutes pass with no reply to my message. A tiny rock becomes my next calling card, but it's too small and barely makes a sound. I find a bigger one. The clink is louder this time. My adrenaline speeds up at the thought that someone else might've heard it.

Within seconds, Adelina pops into view, a finger pressed against her lips, gesturing for me not to make more noise. I tuck into the shadows for invisibility, then wait until she finally flicks the porch light on and walks around the bend of the house.

"Excuse me. May I help you?" she whispers playfully. "It's about time you got here. Did you walk from the Bronx?"

"Well, I didn't realize you lived in the boondocks when I agreed to this."

"I'm just messing with you. Your timing is perfect. I was waiting for my sister to leave and my parents to fall asleep. You have to be as quiet as possible, okay?"

We ninja creep through the living room. The need to keep quiet causes me to become hyper-conscious of every tiptoe and breath. We go up the stairs and into her room. Adelina shuts the door gently behind us. The hood of my coat – which has been shielding me since I left the Bronx – comes off. Her reaction is difficult to decipher in the screen of a beer commercial that has darkened the room.

"What do you think?" I ask anxiously.

Adelina feels up on my head.

"It looks so good, baby. You look like a completely different person."

She unzips my coat and helps me out of it. Once I've settled in, she puts on *The Rocky Horror Picture Show*.

"This is one of my favorite movies ever." she shares.

A glimpse into this other side of her intrigues me. We manage to watch two minutes of the film before our limbs are tangled and tongues just the same. The night eases into salmon and deep blues of a morning sky. Somewhere between the pillow talk, we fall asleep, enamored with the potential of us.

CUPID'S ARROW

The girls at TLC welcome me back with mixed reactions to my new look. Their opinions range from loving it to hating it, sprinkled with a collective celebration over my return. Everyone except Cheri is happy to see me again. She barely acknowledges my presence or the new look when we pass each other in the hallway. After a few failed attempts at conversation, I resign myself to an afternoon *novela*, some reading, and finally a nap. Two hours have gone by with zero clients scheduled and no walk-ins. Anxiety has officially infiltrated my return to this reality by the time Adelina arrives.

"What's up bitches?" she storms in.

I play it cool, pretending she hasn't incited a mini-tornado within me. Cheri doesn't look up from the magazine she's been thumbing through. Adelina kisses me on the cheek, close enough to my mouth that I'm left wanting more, even though we've both agreed to keep our fling private while we're here. The restraint turns me on. She looks over at Cheri on her way back out of the lounge, but they say nothing to each other.

When Adelina returns in new, seductive lingerie, I know she's focused on booking clients today. For me, it's the complete opposite. I'm sitting here wishing with all my energy that no one comes in, especially now that she's here.

I watch her decompress – which always begins with a drink – then she grabs a chair across from Cheri. I'm the only one that seems to notice the tension cutting air between them. My longing to be around Adelina draws me there, too.

"Have you ladies decided what you're doing for Valentine's Day?" I ask.

"Wait, we haven't talked about our plans," Adelina turns to Cheri. "have you picked a place yet?"

"Oh, I'm sorry," she replies sarcastically. "Did I forget to tell you? I have a real Valentine now. Sorry, plans changed."

She tilts her head and gives Adelina a barren smile, then moves from the table to the couch. I watch quietly, asking questions with my eyes. Adelina reaches into her bag and pulls out a pen and a bright, multi-colored notepad. Some words get scribbled on the page, then the pad is pushed over to me:

We got into a huge argument last night over you.

I read it and write:

Over me? Why?

I pass it back.

Adelina writes again and shoves it my way, her body language more aggressive this time. I read on:

She doesn't think we should get serious about each other. And that I'm leading you on and will lose interest fast because I'm not a real "lesbian." She isn't either, but she still liked you, right? Why is it so hard to believe that I could feel things for you, too? Does this mean I'm gay? I hope not.

Her words annoy me. What if I do end up heartbroken again? Things have felt different since I was with her this weekend. The one question that could shatter a lesbian's heart, and I just had to ask.

"What do you identify as?"

It wasn't the question that hurt. It was her answer.

"Straight."

The inquiry must've weighed heavily on her, as

well. Before sneaking me back out, she explained that her parents could never meet me because she didn't want them to think she was gay. I write back:

What if you do hurt me?

Adelina doesn't put pen to paper as quickly as before. She considers her answer for a moment. Then writes:

I promise I won't.

She follows my eyes as I read and look up at her. "I promise." she mouths inaudibly.

I grab the pen and ask another question:

Will you be my Valentine?

Circle one:

Yes!

No :(

Adelina bites her bottom lip and smiles while making her selection. Yes, gets checked off. Cheri throws dirty looks at our classified conversation. Her only access is the grin on my face.

"I guess I've found my real Valentine, too," Adelina announces to the room.

She leans in and plants her juicy, lip-glossed mouth to mine. So much for keeping our relationship hidden.

Later in the day, we play a game of Truth or Dare and Never Have I Ever. Brandy calls for a game of Seven Minutes in Heaven, but Adelina and I are the only ones who want to be locked up alone for that long. We sentence ourselves to our own private game in one of the rooms.

She climbs me like a palm tree as soon as the door closes. Her legs wrap around my waist, soft hands on my face and head – she snakes her tongue into my mouth lustfully. My fingers dig into the curves of her thighs, searching for the parts that are now open to me. A silky touch along her clit invites me to go deeper. The moisture leads the way to her most inner parts.

Our kissing intensifies.

The air is drenched in sex as she slides off of me. I grab ice from the bucket and make my way up her leg, allowing the cube, cleverly placed against my tongue, to trail her skin.

Lola trembles.

Lust rages between our bodies. Her nails pierce into my flesh with an appetite for pleasure. We drift to the loveseat, removing our clothes during the transition, naked by the time we get there. My pussy merges with her pussy as our juices mix. A slight desperation creeps in as we pound into each other over and over.

Lola.

No, Adelina looks heavenly as she slips into the urgency of an orgasm. Her writhing body keeps its rhythm against mine. The strokes change suddenly. An arched back releases one final jolt as she pulls me in, hips still rocking in slow motion.

"You better not hurt me, Sol," she says with sadness in her eyes.

"I promise I won't." A mirror of her pledge to me.

We return to Brandy, venting about her classes at Columbia University and how expensive it is.

"I only took this job to pay for my textbooks," she complains.

Day turns into night without one client coming in. Just as I hoped. On my way home, I pick up a copy of my trusty sidekick, the *Village Voice*. The pages are filled with ads and coupons for all your Valentine's day needs. Our plans are set into motion with reservations at a beautiful Italian restaurant in the Theater District and tickets to the perfect Broadway show. I find a flower shop near TLC that sells exotic flowers. My favorites are these Persian pink and white ones, with both colors running parallel on each bud.

Love is in the air. When the day finally arrives, Papi has our chocolates waiting on the dining room table like clockwork. Adelina's roses have already been delivered when I get to TLC. The arrangement is displayed prominently at the center of the table, while Lola and Cheri are cackling like birds.

"The dynamic duo is back at it again, I see."

Lola pulls me into the kitchen.

"Thank you so much for the roses. They're beautiful," she whispers between kisses.

Her excitement leads us to the social circle, where she starts to hand me presents. The first is a small gift bag with a mini heart-shaped box of chocolates inside. A larger box holds five rolled-up joints, ready to be smoked. The card attached reads:

You better share one of these with me. Thank you for walking into TLC that day.

You changed my life.

xoxo,

Your lollipop.

Lola then gives me a small box. It's a black titanium ring with today's date etched on the interior. It slides onto my finger for a perfect fit.

"I measured it on my mine to make sure it was the right size." Adelina beams proudly while handing me the final gift of chocolate-covered strawberries from Godiva.

I serve us wine to pair with the sweets and give her a rundown of our plans later, without giving away any specific details.

"Girls, we have a client coming in. Please get ready." Becca yells from the front.

Her announcement shifts my mood instantly. The possibility of dealing with a client today slaps me back to reality. It's too easy to forget what has become of my life. I wonder who the client is, but prefer not to ask. If it turns out to be someone who might choose me, the suspense will have me disintegrating in a corner somewhere. Blistex becomes my lip enhancer instead of the seductive red lipstick I've been using. Color-pops make you more likely to be chosen; a reminder to myself.

I'm startled out of a daydream that involves Lola and these strawberries when the doorbell buzzes. My heart is pounding, and my fingertips feel flushed. I say a mental prayer:

Please, God, don't let them pick me.

Becca walks in, and we lock eyes.

"The Wolf is here," she whispers. "he wants a session with you, but I suggested he see your new look first."

An elevator drop sinks into the pit of my stomach. I'm grateful that Becca had this thought, but I hate presenting myself for his approval. Why does he think this is okay after the last session?

Remember, this is a game. Stay in your power.

This internal pep talk keeps me grounded. The embarrassment dissolves instantly. My new look helps me feel more "butch" as I walk. There's a lightness in the fuzz of my hair. It feels good to know that I'm not seeking his validation or money.

I AM NOT FOR SALE!

"Hi, how are you?" I shake his hand with a false grip.

"What did you do to your hair?" he wears the shock across his face like a gushing wound. "This isn't what I imagined when Becca said you had a new look."

"I wanted a change."

"It's terrible. You look so ugly. Did you pay for this?" the Wolf is disgusted.

"You think so? I actually love it. This is the exact look I was going for. I guess I'm not your girl today, huh?"

"Obviously not." he scoffs.

Becca offers to help with his selection process as I exit. I'm hesitant about celebrating too quickly, though. The Wolf has a masochistic streak that holds him hostage to this place. Our brief interaction could leave him wanting more of my indifference.

Becca re-enters the lounge and approaches Cheri this time. He's made his decision. The relief that untethers me causes a blur in my consciousness. I have to stop working here. Tension in my core and across my shoulders has become a daily thing. The corners of my eyes are wet with tears – a bittersweet blend of redemption and rejection.

I speak to Becca in private and tell her that this will be my last day. Each time someone comes in, I find a new hiding spot and stay out of sight. Today's hint of amorous festivities brings a total of thirteen clients by 5:30 p.m. Lola gets booked by four of them. The green-eyed, snot-nosed monster referred to as jealousy feasts within. My imagination, with a mind of its own, creates various scenarios that I play voyeur to.

A food run saves me from any more torture. When I return, Lola has changed into casual clothes but looks just as good. Keeping the plans from her is challenging as she probes for hints.

There are noticeable differences between Lola and Adelina. Tonight, she presents the latter. This side of her is more vulnerable yet just as flirtatious. I pull her chair closer to mine as the world around us becomes background buzz. The climate of love and good food proves to be an aphrodisiac.

After dinner, we walk through the icy streets of Midtown. Orange and white smokestacks vaporize steam towards the night sky. Our mouth imitates them with puffs of body heat escaping us. We pass different theaters showcasing bright lights and names. Adelina's eyes are glowing with curiosity. The walk leads us up Broadway, then a left on 50th street. As soon as she notices the marquee with red letters and a big mouth smiling back at her, she knows.

The Rocky Horror Show

"No way! Is that where we're going?" she squeals.

"Maybe." I flash a deliberately devilish grin.

"You just scored major points right now."

Adelina's excitement is contagious. She rambles on over the cult-like phenomenon surrounding the film and how it's a parody of classic B horror and Sci-fi genres like Frankenstein and Nosferatu.

"Are you talking nerd to me?" I tease, secretly loving everything about her passionate rant.

This cult following she talked about is alive and well as we're ushered to our seats. A majority of the audience is dressed in campy costumes – like the woman dressed in leather and mesh, holding a stuffed cat, and glittered from head to toe. Then there's the pencil-thin, white boy dancing across from us in a turquoise mini skirt with a gold top, dirty combat boots, and a neon yellow boa wrapped around his neck in sheer glamour. The energy is vibrant, filled with laughter and friends finding each other in the crowd. I watch in amazement, taking in this majestic gathering of weirdos and loving Adelina for putting me onto all of it. Our conversation pulses to the current of the collective spirit.

The audience is just as animated once the show begins. Random statements are yelled out, timed perfectly to whatever the actor's following line is. The delivery is so calculated that I can't tell if they're improvising or if the outbursts are actually from the movie.

Lightning shakes the stage.

Adelina heckles this time:

"I don't care where you come, as long as you clean it up!"

The crowd roars into laughter.

Fire sprinklers serve as indoor drizzle, and we're instructed to pull out newspapers from under the seats to cover our heads. Confetti pops from every corner when Eddie, the zombie ex-lover, rides out like a renegade on his motorcycle and closes out the show.

"That was one of the best experiences ever, Solei!" she praises as we walk out of the theater, still dizzy from the spectacle of it all.

Despite freezing temperatures, we drag our feet to the train station, buying ourselves extra time.

"Do you want to be my girlfriend?" Adelina blurts out.

"What?"

Making it "official" was part of the master plan in wooing her tonight. The clock just ran out on me as I worked up the nerve to ask.

"Sure." This vain attempt at playing it cool lasts two seconds before it gets fumbled. "I mean, yeah! Absolutely. I would like that a lot."

Stop talking, Sol.

I finally get myself to shut up and kiss her. We make out for way too long under the world-renowned shine of Times Square until we eventually part ways. My walk continues to the 2-train under the glow of neon billboards, cheesing like a dweeb because I now have a girlfriend.

NYC PRIDE

It's been months since Adelina became my girl-friend. After Valentine's Day, she joined me in the real world, leaving behind TLC's under-ground and inebriated existence.

June in New York City can only mean one thing. All the queers, whether gay, trans, straight, everything in between and all around, can be found in the West Village – especially the pier at Christopher Street.

Adelina meets me in the train station with one goal in mind; to find a tattoo shop. It won't be hard in this part of town. The one city block of 6ᵗʰ Ave. and West 4ᵗʰ has at least four to choose from. The guy behind the counter of the shop we go into, is covered in piercings and ink all over his body. His tongue is split in half like a serpent. I only know this because he's swirling the two halves around each other as he watches us enter.

"How much to get each other's names tattooed?"

"Do you have I.D. to prove you're old enough to do such a stupid thing?" he responds dryly.

"Yeah, we do," I reply boldly, assuming he knows nothing about real love.

"What are your names? Where do you want them, and how big?" he gives us a binder filled with different font styles.

We pick the same calligraphy and size after some deliberation. Mine is simple; her name scrolled up my wrist in small letters. It takes him fifteen minutes to finish it. Adelina, on the other hand, pulls down her pants to hang at the hips. The tattoo artist shakes his head when she tells him to brand her private area with my name. I watch in awe as the waxed surface of skin absorbs the ink.

The placement of Adelina's tattoo shocks me into a slight obsession. If there was ever a way to profess your undying love for someone, this is it. She doesn't complain once as the needle penetrates inch by inch in rapid-fire. The only thing I have to gauge of her level of discomfort is how she's biting her bottom lip – which she also does when she's turned on – making it even harder to interpret. When he's finished, I press my face into hers.

"I love you."

"You fucking better," she smiles.

We get ice cream afterward and find a spot to people watch.

"I'm bleaching my hair tomorrow for the parade,"

I reveal.

"Really? When did you decide that? And when were you planning on asking me?" she says playfully.

"I kinda just decided that I'm going to bleach it for the summer, then grow it back in September."

Adelina's expression changes when her eyebrows scrunch up in the center of a tense forehead waging war.

"Wait, you're growing your hair back? Why? You're gonna look like such a girl."

"I am a girl!"

"Right, but you don't look like one."

"You do remember asking me to be your girlfriend, right? Have I misled you on the fact that I'm a girl?"

"Don't be sarcastic. I'm serious." she rolls her eyes.

Adelina starts to get emotional.

"I am, too. I never planned on keeping my hair short. I just wanted a fresh start. And now, every time I get a haircut, my mother loses her shit. There are even times when she inspects my hairline and convinces herself that I've cut it when I haven't. I need to grow it back soon, so she can leave me alone."

"Are you serious? You should've told me this before I got your name tattooed on my body forever. I would've thought twice about it!" she yells.

None of my words feel valid enough for a response to this argument. The clash between us takes root and grows into my biggest fear right before my eyes.

Regret.

"You're already regretting our tattoos?"

"If you're going to start looking like a girl again, then yes."

"Adelina, growing my hair won't change me. I'm still the same person, whether my hair is short or long. It's just hair."

"No, it's not!" she explodes. "How you wear it is

an important factor in what you're presenting to the world." Tears fall from her eyes.

"Why are you crying?"

"That would mean I like girls, and I don't!" she yells, while ignoring my question.

"Okay, fine. So, you're a few notches away from me on the Kinsey scale of sexuality. Who gives a shit?"

"No, like I'm on the complete opposite side."

She stops talking and stares off into space. I'm not sure if it's guilt for being mean or from realizing what she's trying to say.

How do I even fix this?

"We have a serious problem then. Just because I'm a lesbian with short hair doesn't mean I don't want to be a girl."

My eyes remain fixed on the city moving on around us. It's hard enough being a woman in this crazy world. Now I have to navigate this new reality with my girlfriend. Should I even call her that anymore?

"I know what you are." Adelina salvages. "I might not like girls, but I love you. This style just makes me feel more comfortable about us."

"Well, I like you better in stilettos than sneakers. We can compromise here." I attempt to lighten the mood. "I can keep it short after the summer, but eventually, I'm growing it back."

"I'll make sure to talk you out of it again," she giggles and wipes the feelings off her cheek.

Normally, I would hug and kiss her all over until she feels better, but my pride cancels out the desire to comfort her. I lick my own wounds instead. We part ways with careless goodbyes. Adelina hesitates when she realizes the absence of affection in my kiss, but certainty in my departure ends the night.

This bandage protecting the new "body art" on my wrist is a reminder of the dumb shit we did to ourselves.

Hours ago, I was so sure I wanted to be with Adelina forever. Now I'm all doubt tangled into a hairball of anxiety. Her ignorance was so extreme. I rewind every word, over and over, all the way home. Then rinse and repeat while taking a shower.

That would mean I like girls, and I don't!

I am replaying them again as I wash off peroxide under the bathroom sink.

I might not like girls, but I love you.

Laughing at my reflection in the mirror, a bright head of hair stares back at me under the tungsten lights of our bathroom. A resemblance to the rapper Eminem sparks an epiphany. Adelina's going to love this look, and Mami's going to hate it.

My younger sister comes into the bathroom while I decide whether or not I like it. Winnie doesn't have that annoying kid sister thing, but she has her moments.

"Ma, there's a stranger in our bathroom!" she jumps back in full character mode.

"Ha. Ha." I snap.

"No, dude. You can seriously pass for a guy. Is that what you're going for?"

"You sound like Mami. What did she tell you?"

"I mean, have you seen yourself?" Winnie says sarcastically.

"I'm just trying different looks."

"Well, it feels like I have two brothers now, thanks to you." she rolls her eyes. "The other day, Rocky was swooning over you. It was so disgusting."

I see Winnie's point. Rocky has been her best friend since they were seven years old.

"Can I have some privacy now?" I change the topic.

The clash between my mother and Adelina's wishes projected on to me is more than enough to drown in. I haven't thought about how Winnie was processing all of these changes I'm going through.

Things haven't been the same between us since I ran away from home a few years ago. She was thirteen at the time. It was right after my Sweet Sixteen. My parents threw me a huge party to celebrate, but Mami's strict rules were suffocating me. Instead of giving me more freedom, she was getting stricter. And I knew exactly why. It was a domino effect that had started the year before.

"Mami, can I talk to you about something?"

Her bruja instincts understood this would be a serious talk as Mami's back straightened up in bed. We had just gotten back from shopping at the mall in Yonkers. The high I felt from retail therapy and bonding with my mother gave me the *cojones* to finally speak my truth.

Mami had a whole other set of fears that began to surface.

"Are you pregnant?"

I shook my head at how far off she was. Maybe her

intuition wasn't as sharp as I thought.

"What? No. That's not what I want to talk about, Ma. Just listen to me."

Mami was upset before she heard what I had to say; her left leg already bouncing from impatience.

"I'm sexually attracted to girls."

Disclosing this classified information to my mother erupted into World War III at the house of Romero. This woman's rage sloshed through each room – her offensive words saturating the walls in thick, gooey judgment.

"Prefiero que sea puta que pata!"

A smear campaign that toured every level of the house, informing anyone listening that she would rather I "be a whore, than a lesbian." Things haven't been the same in my family since that day. A year after that failed talk, I ran away from home. During that time, my father had a stroke, but Winnie suffered the most because we were always together up until that point. Papi told me about sleepless nights, where she would come down crying at 2 a.m. Her grades dropped that year, and they even took her to see a therapist. All because I wanted to run the streets lawlessly.

My dismissal isn't enough to make Winnie go away, though. She's still standing in the bathroom watching me.

"I'm tired of everyone giving their unsolicited opinions on how I should look."

Why does everyone get hung up on gender roles and hair length? Or what someone should or shouldn't do and wear. I've always found androgynous types to be the most interesting characters. Give me Angelina Jolie in *Gia* or Michelle Rodriguez in an action movie any day.

"What does that even mean?" Winnie carries on with the topic at hand. "Who else is pressuring you to grow your hair?"

"The opposite."

"Oh."

"Adelina wants me to keep it short. She freaked out and started crying and everything." I admit, feeling the need to vent.

"But why?" Winnie objects.

"Because then the world sees that she's in a same-sex relationship."

"Um. That's weird. Did she not notice your boobs?"

"Exactly what I said."

"You need to drop that bitch, immediately."

"No, wait… it gets better."

Winnie's eyeballs nearly pop out of their sockets when I remove the piece of gauze covering the tattoo. She sees Adelina's name crusting the top layers of my skin then throws a fit.

"Hell no! Is that real? That better not be real, Solei. Why? Why would you do that?"

She's now at a full pace back and forth in the hall-way.

"Mami's going to kick you out. Again. No. She's going to kill you, then kick you out!"

My poor sister doesn't have the stomach to deal with our mother's fury. Every time Mami throws a tan-trum, Winnie becomes flushed in warm, rosy cheeks of nerves. If it's a more intense fight, she'll break out in hives. At this moment, she's in the pale turning phase – which is like a level two out of five. It isn't higher because our parents aren't home at the moment.

"It's not that serious." I suck my teeth at her in denial, knowing deep down that she's right about the outcome of these actions.

My response is a long-winded rant about my rights of being the ripe old age of, *I'm an adult now.* The more I ram-ble, the more Winnie panics. With her anxiety now surfac-ing as nail-biting. If there's anything my sensitive younger sister hates, it's a confrontation of any kind with anyone.

"Do me a favor and act like I don't know any-thing."

"Fine. You're good. Tattoo? What tattoo?"

Some sisterly support would've been great since I'm the one actually going through it. There must be a planetary shift going on or something.

Note to self:

Find out which planet is retrograding and fix it.

Winnie gives up on me and locks herself back up in her room. The fact that the parentals will be returning soon puts an extra pep in my step. I'm not ready to face my mother yet, especially with this bleached hair and name branded on me.

The whole crew walks to Crotona Park for night pool. That's the name we came up with for sneaking into the park after midnight. One of the guys from the block has it down to a science.

"If we sneak in during shift change, we got two hours before they come back."

The time always flies by quickly before we're forced to scatter like insects under the spotlights. Sammy and I call it a night once the cops crash the party. We're too excited about tomorrow's pride festivities.

The following day, I start extra early. Sammy stays in bed. Semi-naked gay boys, lesbians in wife-beaters flexing their muscled tattoo sleeves, trans *mamis* and *papis*, and drag queens are filling the city. They are performance-ready in bright colors and feathers coming out of everywhere. I walk past a squad of scantily clad femmes strutting all their goodies, followed by stone-cold butches, making sure no one disrespects them. And me, wandering with nothing to do because I woke up feeling stir-crazy.

There's a line going around the block at the one place serving breakfast. I spot an old friend halfway to getting in, who tells me they now identify as nonbinary and invite me to cut the line to join them and their friends. I realize the group is loud and obnoxious after accepting the invitation.

It's too early for this shit.

My desire to socialize is ruined by the stares and disapproving eyes gazing back at us. The loudest one of the friends feeds off the attention and acts more outrageous by the second. His tribe encourages the hype with suggestions on what poses to hold while they take pictures.

"Give me face, bitch," one instigates.

I'm supposed to call Adelina to figure out today's plans, but I'm not sure I want to. Her name on my wrist is taunting me. I wish I could rub it raw until it's gone. The permanence of this mistake feels more shackling than having a kid with someone you can't stand.

The gay boys are now "voguing" and challenging one another to dance-offs with no music playing.

That's my cue to exit before it gets worse. I finally give in to calling Adelina.

"It's about time. I've been waiting for your call all morning, stupid."

"Why are you calling me stupid?"

"I don't mean it like that. It's just a figure of speech." she dismisses. "What took you so long? You never sleep this late."

"I'm already downtown. Where do you want to meet?"

Adelina starts to argue with me when she hears that I'm in the city without her. The day hasn't even kicked off, and I'm already in a bad mood. It takes a few minutes to explain why I'm avoiding my mother and another ten to rationalize my thought process in not going to her first.

"Come pick me up. I'll start getting ready now."

Click.

How did I get hustled into going all the way to Queens, just to come right back? When I get there forty-five minutes later, she's still not ready, of course. It takes another half-hour before she finally turns the corner of her block, looking shy. Adelina always acts like this when we argue. The temporary modesty gets overshadowed by her ripped up, rhinestone-studded shirt – an Adelina original – hot pink skinny jeans, stilettos, and her favorite heart-shaped sunglasses.

She kisses me with a warmth I can't reciprocate. Her scattered topics are strung along in tangents as I pretend to keep up. Adelina is oblivious to the fact that I barely like her right now.

"Babe, I'm sorry... your hair looks amazing. I meant to say that, but you know how my brain works." she waves her disregard off as a joke.

As we make our way through the swelling crowd against the police barricades, thousands of people celebrating pride cross our path. Every other street corner aligns me with someone I know from different chapters of my life. The interaction is usually the same. It starts with big hugs.

"Oh, my God!"

"What are you doing here?"

"It's been so long!"

"You're gay now?"

"This is my girlfriend."

"Let's party later."

"I owe you a drink!"

The exchanges usually end with an agreement to link up later, but you rarely do. You never have to, though, because you end up at the same parties trying to get the bartender's attention.

Sammy and Natalia finally find us along the route.

"I have to pee." Adelina rudely announces, interrupting the moment I'm having with my best friend.

Sammy cups her hands together.

"Here you go, sweetie."

"Can we find a bathroom, please?" Adelina disregards her.

"Come on. We'll all go." Sammy offers.

"No, you can stay here. Hopefully, we'll lose you. I mean, hopefully, we won't lose you."

After fifteen minutes of waiting in line at the pizza shop, we all decide to use it. I'm the last to come back out, where I find Sammy and Natalia ordering a slice. Adelina is nowhere in sight.

"Yo, where's my girl?" I ask.

"I just saw her walk out."

I can see Adelina on the sidewalk talking to a shirtless guy on a motorcycle. His nipples are covered in stickers that read:

I'm a Lesbian.

The crowd shields me enough to observe their interaction. Her body language tells me all I need to know about the conversation, as she laughs at something he says and touches his arm. The guy hands Adelina his phone – sending me into action. I move through the crowd towards them, but she spots me in time and walks away from him.

"Who was that?" I demand.

"Who?"

Her attitude teeters between:

"I've been caught!" and "why are you questioning me?"

"Um, that guy you were just talking to."

I point him out of the crowd as his boys celebrate his phone number acquisition in the middle of gay pride.

"Oh… he's… this guy I know."

The hesitation buys her time to think.

"Really? From where?"

Adelina's eyebrows scrunch up as they do when she gets defensive.

"Are you kidding me? Sol, if I tell you I know somebody, then I know them. I don't have a reason to lie."

Her argument is so firm that a feeling of foolishness starts to sink in. It doesn't feel like the truth, though. I know what I saw. I've never doubted anything she has ever told me until right now.

"Okay, so why did he shake your hand like he was introducing himself to you?"

"He was… joking around. Pretending to… be introducing himself because it's been a while."

I'm not sure what bothers me more. The fact that she thinks I'm this dumb or that she's such a terrible liar. Skepticism escapes me in the form of a chuckle. My face is hard with anger as my jaw clenches so tight I can feel grinding on the enamel of my teeth.

An assembly line of fellow parade-goers flash, prance, strut, and swagger on the congested corner of Christopher and Hudson. I want to be fabulous with them, but here I am, angry at my girlfriend for flirting with some fuckboy. I should've left her ass at home.

Adelina kisses me.

This failed attempt to reel me back in sparks rebellion instead. Determined to be an asshole, I flirt with drunken hot girls as they walk by. The music from the float passing through is turning the streets into one big party. One extra-lit spectator presses her butt into me and starts to *dutty wine*. A friend grabs the girl and yanks her away.

"Hey, come here. Don't start your shit. I know what you're doing. Please, don't." Adelina puts her arm around my waist and presses into me.

"You're the one that started acting single."

"*We're* not single, okay? Your eyes better stay on

me," she demands.

"That goes both ways." I push back from her, "I saw you give that guy your number."

"Baby, he got the wrong number. I was just trying to be polite, so I went along with it."

Adelina wraps her arms around my waist again, claiming me. I turn to putty in her persistence, even though I know she's lying. This deception is a salve to my hurting heart. Choosing denial allows me permission to forgive her.

Sammy and Natalia return to us being romantic, unaware of our little fight. It takes two hours to get through the crowd for a good view of the fireworks at the end of the night.

"Can you take me home, baby?" Adelina pouts like a kid trying to get her way. "I'll sneak you in. I want you to sleep with me tonight."

Sammy interrupts her.

"Aren't we going to Cottontail? You know they

throw the best pride parties."

"Are you crazy? My feet are killing me. I've been in heels all day." Adelina whines.

"No one said you had to come. I meant we as in us." Sammy uses her index finger to create a circle that excludes Adelina.

I cut them off before it escalates.

"I'm taking her home. I can't let her go by herself." Adelina grins victoriously. "I'll drop her off and meet you at the club in like two hours." I turn to her, "I would love to spend the night, but I don't want to hide under the bed for hours while your parents fall asleep or because they woke up early in the morning."

Adelina's expression breaks triumph as she realizes my plan is different from hers. She stomps down the steps of the subway station in protest.

"I'll find you at Cottontail," I tell Sammy before rushing behind her.

It's hard to keep an eye on Adelina through the wave of people descending onto the platform until she stops by a payphone to wait for the train. A few feet away from where she has posted up is the group from this morning. They're still "voguing" and challenging each other for the best moves. Adelina sucks her teeth and folds her arms when she sees me.

"I don't need you to take me home. Go have fun with your little friends."

The gay boys erupt into cackles.

"Why are you upset? Is it so hard to understand why I don't want to hide under your bed instead of partying with my friends?"

Adelina lightens up. Her shoulders relax, and her eyebrows straighten out.

"I just want you in my bed. It's been such a great day that I don't want it to end."

She's using "great day" very loosely, hardly believing it herself.

"I know, love. Not tonight, though. All right?"

Just then, one of the gay boys shrieks like a girl.

"Shut up already, will ya?" A disheveled white man yells out at them. "I'm tired of you fags making all this goddamn noise. Acting like a bunch of pussies."

His words are slurred.

"I know that motherfucker isn't talking to me." one member of the group mumbles.

There's a pronounced difference from the flamboyant behavior they've had on display.

"Men acting like women, it's crazy!" the rant continues.

I pull away from Adelina, aware of something deeper brewing, but my goal of not attracting his attention is sabotaged when he stares right at us.

"Now we have dudes with tits! Unbelievable. You're all going to hell. Every last one of you!"

Adelina fidgets and focuses on the tunnel for an incoming train.

"Is that your girlfriend, little boy?" he laughs. "Hey! I'm talking to you."

"Listen, I don't want any trouble. I'm just trying to get home, all right?"

"You don't want any trouble? Should've thought of that before turning into a big, fat dyke."

His words weigh me down like cinder blocks at the bottom of a lake.

Dyke.

The word doesn't bother me all that much. It's how it gets flung like a ninja star when a man wants to insult your sexuality. This particular man is still going off from his holier-than-thou high horse about why he's superior to all of us. Each statement brings him one step closer.

"Yo, why are you coming into our personal space?" I finally push back. "And why are you in the village if you hate gay people so much?"

"You're all living in sin. You'll burn in hell for it," he shouts.

"Get out of here with that shit, bro."

"Bro? I'm not your fucking bro. You think you're a man? I'll treat you like a man."

He charges at me with closed fists. My face gets pummeled with punches three times.

Right.

Left.

Right.

On the third hit, everything blacks out.

My brain regains consciousness before the rest of me does. Whatever machine is beeping near me is causing my head to pound. Through the slits of puffed skin, I can see a blurred hospital room. Everything hurts. Someone's silhouette is in the corner watching over me.

"Baby," I whisper, assuming it's Adelina.

The person jumps up from their chair.

"Hey, it's Sammy. Some asshole attacked you. Do you remember?" her voice is unsettled.

"Yeah, that idiot was acting so dumb. Where's Adelina?" I mumble.

"I don't know. She texted me from your phone saying you were being brought to this hospital. When I got here, she was gone."

"Can you call my parents?"

"I already did. They're on the way. Oh, and if the nurses ask, I'm your sister."

"How bad does my face look?"

Every part of my face and head feels swollen and lumped up. I must look like an ogre.

"I'll be honest, it doesn't look cute, but I have a plan. We'll tell the ladies you're a boxer, and I'm your coach. We're going to get so much play." she chuckles.

Sammy's game plan is amusing, but it hurts too much to express it.

My parents wait outside the hospital until we're done. Winnie is in the backseat, her wide eyes filled with concern. I recount the fragments of what I can remember as they listen quietly. The tension is tangible beneath their calm exteriors. Details of this random man beating me up fall under the worst things they have warned me about. This story is a scary confirmation that the world will pass its judgment on their daughter for the lifestyle she lives.

"Can we get something to eat?" I ask.

We unanimously agree on a diner uptown. When Sammy tries to convince Papi to let her pay for her share, he goes straight into papa bear mode.

"Get your mom some flowers with that money."

I rest my eyes on the drive back home. My neck is starting to cramp up from the punches thrown at me. Visions of that moment on the platform pop into my mind – the gay boys, the drunk asshole, the people watching in shock, and Adelina roll around in my head. A train on the opposite track pulls in. It screeches to a stop then hisses with relief.

First blow to the head.

The gay boys scream and rush to defend me.

Second blow to the head.

I catch a glimpse of Adelina with a disturbed look on her face.

"You want to be a man? Hit me back!"

I throw a weak punch that barely connects.

Third blow to the head.

The tallest of the gay boys punches the drunk guy before my world blacks out. They turned out to be my heroes in all of this. When I hit the floor in my mind's eye, my body jumps in the physical.

BOYS DON'T CRY

Home becomes a prison as my bruises heal. Adelina has called me so many times that I've turned my phone off. Every couple of hours, the house line rings. Mami tells whoever is on the other end that I'm not home. By Thursday of the following week, all the swelling has gone down. The black-and-blues are now lavender and yellow. Marco has given me the green light to go back to work on Monday. Makeup will have to cover any remaining evidence of the assault.

I throw on a hat and sunglasses for a bike ride into the city and back, making it as far as 110th Street and Central Park on the hood side. The landscape is a perfect mix of New York City's grit and the natural elements we co-exist with.

A group of badass kids run by me, holding a turtle they've pulled out of the lake. I'm worried for the little guy. It could go a couple of different ways. They either want him as a pet, an experiment, or somebody's momma is about to make some soup.

When I return home hours later, Adelina is sitting on the front steps of the house.

"Hi." she greets me humbly as I walk my bike into the yard.

"Hey."

"Your face... take your shades off."

"I don't want to. What are you even doing here?"

"*Hello*, I've been calling like a maniac. I'm only

here because you haven't answered, and your mother demanded I stop calling. Why are you avoiding me?"

"Why do you think I would be ignoring you? Any idea at all? Like, maybe leaving me alone at the hospital after someone attacked me?"

Seeing Adelina brings back all the anger from that day. It takes everything inside of me to not go off on her. The only reason I was even on that platform was because of her. Maybe if she would've worn flats like a regular person, we would've still been with my friends.

"I've never been through anything like that, Sol. I didn't know what to do."

"I've never been through anything like that, either." I interrupt. "It felt so fucked up when I realized you weren't there."

"I couldn't see you like that. And at least I called Sammy to come to the hospital before leaving."

It hurts to have my hands pressed against my face,

but I don't want her to see the tears starting to form.

"I need time to myself. I'm not done healing physically, and still need to get over what you did to me. I would never abandon you like that."

"I understand, baby. Call me if you need anything. I love you, don't forget that."

A small part of me wants to reciprocate her, "I love you," but I'm too angry.

Papi is right where I left him watching TV.

"Hi, *muñeca*. Did you see that girl? She came looking for you."

"Yeah, I saw her, Pa. Thanks."

"Oh, okay." he drops the topic. "Your face is looking better."

"Yeah, if you think gremlins are cute."

"You're in luck. I do think gremlins are cute."

Papi's watching one of his old-school movies. He's down for anything that has fight scenes and explosions.

I'm convinced he thinks Clint Eastwood is his spirit animal. Despite being exhausted, I decide to stay downstairs and watch the movie with him. My resistance doesn't last long before sleep comes for me. When my father wakes me up with a nudge, I can't tell how much time has passed, but the movie has ended, and the TV isn't on anymore. He's holding the house phone in one hand and covering the mouthpiece with the other.

"It's Adelina," he whispers.

I shake my head, but he passes the phone anyway.

"Hello?"

"Hi, my love," she greets me like everything is okay between us. "I just wanted to let you know I got home safe. And it was really good to see you today. I hope we can get past this and makeup soon."

Hearing her voice in this half-asleep state brings down my guard. Silence is now my only armor against the sweet words. I don't want her to know they're working.

"I'm staying in tonight," she continues. "I'm going to watch *Boys Don't Cry* with my sister."

The thing I miss most is staying up late watching movies together. Throughout our relationship, she has put me on to a whole list of classics. I've never cried watching a film until I met Adelina.

"Okay, enjoy." I keep it short and conceal my vulnerability.

"Call me, if anything," she adds. "I'll keep the phone next to me all night."

"Okay." I drop the call before she can say anything else.

Papi has now retreated to whatever project he's working on downstairs. The living room is dark, except for the light coming from his workstation. A headache pounds away at my brain – a constant since that violent encounter. I take a warm bath and go to bed.

The only dreams I can remember now are haunted ones. Tonight's nightmares are filled with images of Adelina riding past me on a bicycle. She's dressed in one of her favorite outfits from TLC. The location changes. My attacker sits next to me at a bar. His hand is on my leg as he leans in for a kiss. A beer bottle nearby becomes my weapon as I smash his head with all of my force. He laughs at my weakness as my swing barely hits. Women dancing half-naked on the bar are now the gay boys dressed in drag with distorted faces.

The blue glow off my screen reads 3:33 a.m. as I jump out of my sleep. The summer heat has me drenched in sweat. Someone in the neighborhood is blasting old freestyle songs out of their apartment window. This is a summer ritual in The Bronx. These electronic love songs are like a time warp that Latinos in the tri-state area seem to have gotten stuck in during the 80s and 90s. We will proudly sing our hearts out to these tracks while dipping and weaving our heads, doing "the wop," and pretending to be in music videos.

I rest my head back on the pillow as the song *Without You* by George Lamond plays next. The lyrics make me think of Adelina. In a moment of hopeless romanticism, I decide to call her back.

"Hello," she whispers, half asleep.

"Sorry. I thought you were still up."

"It's okay. Is everything good?"

Silence again. There's so much to say, but I can't find the right words for all the things I'm feeling.

"Nothing... I just, I miss you." I finally admit.

"I miss you too. So much."

"And you suck, but I want things to go back to normal between us," I add.

"Me too, baby. I'm sorry. I prom–"

"Can we not talk about it anymore? I want to forget this ever happened." I cut her off, "How was the movie?"

"It was insane. You have to watch it."

"What's it called again?"

"*Boys Don't Cry*. It's about this woman who feels like she was born the wrong gender. She goes around passing as a man, and people believe her." Adelina explains.

"Okay, so she's transgender. There are dancers at Krash that are trans."

"I was thinking about how cool it would be if you did that," she says. "You could definitely pass for a guy. Oh my God, that would be such a turn-on."

"A turn-on? Pretending to be a guy? That's what does it for you?"

Adelina explains her logic further.

"You wouldn't have to pretend to be anything. You already look like a dude. All you have to do is hide your breasts and go by a different name. In the movie, she wrapped hers with an elastic bandage and looked completely flat-chested."

"But I don't want to pass as a guy. People that do are embarrassed or disgusted over their unwanted body parts. In their minds, they were born the wrong gender. I don't feel that way. I like my breasts, and I'm perfectly content with being a woman."

Adelina continues trying to explain why it's a good idea. I watch the shadows of cars drive by on my walls as I listen to her.

"It would help us draw less attention. People would think we're a normal couple, and these stupid guys wouldn't bother us as much."

The catcalls and street harassment have gotten worse since the nicer weather came around. Anytime we're out and about, we have random guys trying to get her attention. Most of the time, they pretend not to see me. If they're the aggressive type, they become confrontational and assure us it's because she needs "some real dick in her life" while grilling me up and down. It does something to an insecure man's spirit when he sees an attractive woman dating another woman. If it's two femmes, the male usually wants to get all up in it. He needs the validation that these two women are incomplete without him to balance the scales.

If the other person is not a femme, though – like, a butch or any derivative of a non-feminine woman or non-binary. Forget it. Said male will seek concession by demanding they prove their masculinity or bow down to his.

"So, all you want is for me to hide my breasts?"

"Yes! It would still be you, right? The person I love and adore. It would be us in our own little bubble."

"My mother is going to lose her mind if she finds out about this."

"She doesn't have to. If you wear bigger shirts, it's hard to tell."

Adelina is bursting at the seams. I can hear the stitches popping in her voice.

"All right, I'll try. If it means getting less attention and problems, I'm down for that."

"Really?" she shrieks. "I have the perfect name picked out, too... Tyler!"

"Wait, I have to go by a different name? You didn't say anything about that."

"Yes, I did. And, of course, you do. That's how it was in the movie. Her birth name was Teena Brandon, but she switched it to Brandon Teena to make it manly. Solei and Sol are too girly, and I don't like the sound of Romero. It's too close to Romeo, and that would sound corny. I like Tyler better."

"Tyler sounds mad white, though."

"A name like that makes you sound like a skater boy. You already dress grunge. Your hair is blonde. It's perfect." She drops her voice, "Tyler Love, the love of my life."

All I can do is laugh at her master plan.

"And this is how you solve our problems? From crazy Hollywood movies?"

"It's based on a true story. She really lived like that."

"*He* lived like that." I correct.

"You know what I mean. Anyway, this story got all this attention because some guys found out the truth, and they killed him."

"Are you kidding me right now? Isn't that a huge red flag on why it's not a good idea?"

"Okay, but that was the Midwest. Those people are nuts. We live in the most progressive city in the world. It's different here."

"Yeah? Tell that to the guy that beat me up."

"Perfect example. If you were Tyler, your breasts wouldn't have triggered him."

She's kind of right. That is what set him off. Realizing I'm a girl always triggers them. If they thought I was a guy, I'd get more respect. They definitely wouldn't try to talk to my girl right in front of my face. I try imagining myself living like this in the real world. What was it like for Brandon Teena? Did anyone ever notice something different but couldn't quite put their finger on it? I mean, it wouldn't be that far of a stretch for me. I've always been a tomboy. Growing up, I wanted to be just like my brother, Kelvin. I would borrow his baggy jeans for dress-down days at school. Mami always bought mine too tight around the hips. I didn't like the attention they drew from older men lurking outside the bodega.

"All right, I'll be your boyfriend. Under one condition, though. You're going to have to do some things in return."

She jumps at the offer.

"Deal. This is going to make everything better. Watch."

After the initial rush of our newly formed pact, there isn't much else to talk about. An awkward silence infiltrates the call. We end it before it gets worse.

"Sweet dreams, my Tyler Love. Talk to you tomorrow. I love you." Adelina pierces a juicy kiss through the phone.

"I love you, too."

It takes another couple of days before the swelling and bruises heal up. I can now open both eyes. A small gash above my right eyelid is starting to seal under a scab. I have no plans, but restlessness inspires me out of the house. My first stop is the pharmacy on 3rd Avenue. That is where most of us in the neighborhood go for spontaneous last-minute shopping. The security guard eyes me as I walk in. He's telepathically letting me know that I'm being watched. Each aisle gets a quick scan until I finally find what I'm looking for – bandages. The largest size meant for leg injuries makes the most sense. I pick up a copy of Adelina's favorite fashion magazine and chocolates at the counter.

My next stop is the sporting goods store, where I buy a Yankees fitted cap. On the way back home, I call Adelina.

"Hey, beautiful. It's your lover boy. Can I see you today?"

"Hold on. She's using the bathroom." her sister Betty sighs.

I deepen my voice to sound more masculine.

"Tell her it's Tyler."

The music in the background gets louder, then lowers as her sister opens the door.

"Some girl named Tyler wants to see you, beautiful." she teases.

"Shut up."

The door slams.

"Hi, baby."

"Hey, can I see you today?" I repeat to the right person.

"Of course, where are we meeting?"

"Washington Square Park in two hours."

"Done and done. See you there."

Even though our conversation is brief, it's enough to pull me out of hibernation and go out into the world again. We've been so distant since the pride parade. I miss talking and laughing, and I especially miss kissing her. Mirrored closet doors in my bedroom reflect a newly emerging persona. First, the shirt comes off, then the tank top, and finally, my sports bra. The elasticity in the bandage starts to mask the femininity. I pull tighter, making sure they flatten as much as possible. I can barely breathe by the time they're fully wrapped.

The Velcro makes a crunching sound as it fights to keep its ends together. There's instant comfort when it's loosened for me to try again, this time stretching the fabric way less for a better fit, but it's still very constricting. The tank top and shirt go back on while I study myself in the mirror, hardening my face to avoid exposing any tenderness. The Yankees cap fits perfectly – brim pulled down to shadow my eyes, squared up jawline, tightened abs, and a widening in my shoulders to take up more space. Adelina's going to love this.

Leaving home makes me feel like a fugitive on the run, while avoiding anyone that knows my family. This great escape from home and hood leads me to one of the most eclectic spaces in Manhattan; Washington Square Park. This is where performers, artists, activists, skateboarders, NYU students, chess players, Yogis, Hare Krishnas, and undercover cops claim their land.

Two girls walk by me.

"Did you see that cute boy?"

One of them blurts out and turns around to make eye contact. They speed walk away in giggles and girl talk. Adelina scans the park near the benches we usually meet each other at. She doesn't recognize me sitting right in front of her and continues walking.

"Psst."

She doesn't look. I try again. This time more assertive.

"Sol?"

"Nope, Tyler."

"Holy shit! You look way more like a boy than I thought you would. Except you look like you haven't hit puberty yet!" she sits on my lap and kisses me all over my face. "You are so handsome."

"Okay, now it's my turn."

We cut through the crowd and into a department store on Broadway. Adelina follows as I pick a few styles she would look killer in. When no one is looking, we lock ourselves into a fitting room towards the back where gigantic speakers are booming techno music. Adelina performs a striptease while modeling a dress for me. One by one, the outfits bring new levels of sexual tension. Each time an article of clothing is removed, she deliberately bends over with my face aligned just right until her G-string gets pulled off and slipped it into my pocket.

"Oh, it's like that?" she smiles.

"Yup, it's exactly like that."

Adelina takes my hat off and pushes my face into the sweet scent between her legs. The dress falls over my head, creating a vortex where this fitting room is the only place in the world. She lets out a moan. Someone outside of the room chuckles, then low voices gossip to each other.

"Excuse me. The line is getting long out here." A woman knocks on the door.

"Almost done, be right out." Adelina regains her composure.

The whispers continue. When we step out, everyone that is waiting is posted up like judge and jury. An employee folding clothes rolls her eyes at me.

"*Hello*, this is the women's fitting room, you little pervert. That's probably why your face got lumped up, huh?"

I say nothing. It's better to let her think I'm some horny teenage boy than a fully grown, naughty lesbian. We practically run out of the store before anyone else says something.

"Baby! They bought it. You see? It worked!"

"That was weird. It felt like they were going to figure me out." I admit.

"I know! I was hoping you didn't say anything because it would've given you away."

Adelina rambles as we go back to the park. The encounter leaves me feeling strange and excited. I bend the visor of my hat between my hands in a fidget when a petite, black woman in a medicinal pink suit and beige loafers starts zipping through hordes of people. She's offering us her salvation. Christian booklets get pulled from her tote bag. I'm handed one with people running from homes and cars on fire that reads:

Surviving the Rapture!
Renouncing Worldly Pleasures.

Her preaching begins before we have a chance to escape.

"No, thank you, ma'am. Now's not a good time."

The woman stares me down.

"My child, are you a boy or a girl? I honest to God cannot tell."

"You see? It's not that simple," I blow up on Adelina.

"Jesus loves you! Repent now, before it's too late."

A bible becomes the woman's armor as she waves it at me. Escaping once again, I speed walk away from both of them.

"Baby, wait," Adelina yells out.

"You can save yourself! Rebuke these entities controlling you and turn your life over to Jesus. Repent, child!"

Her words an echo chamber to sermons I've been on my knees to in church – and a memory of the moment my ex-girlfriend, Camila's mom, caught us kissing in her room.

Adelina catches up to me.

"Babe, don't let that crazy lady ruin our day."

"This is too much, Adelina."

"Wait, are you blaming me for what just happened?"

"I'm going home. We'll try this whole Tyler thing another day."

I find refuge in the only place I can go with this feeling inside of me. Giselle opens the door when I show up at Sammy's apartment, unannounced. Her sarcasm and jokes are usually met with matched wit or a quirky rebuttal, but I don't have it in me today.

Sammy doesn't hear when I knock three times before giving myself permission to enter. She's blasting slow jams, and taking selfies in her sports bra and boxers in full flex mode.

"What the hell? Can't you see I'm having a photoshoot here?" she grabs a pillow to cover herself.

"Oh, please. I have my own to look at."

"Yo, I swear every time I see you, you're like a completely different person. What's going on with you?"

"Ever since this haircut, things have changed with Adelina. It just keeps escalating more and more." I unload my dirty laundry onto my best friend before even taking a seat.

"And what level is this?"

The shirt comes off to show just how far we've gotten and to remove this damn bandage. My ribs and lungs are sore from being compressed.

"What happened to your tits? Why are you letting

this girl change you?" Her indignation lingers as she inspects the binding.

My defenses go up.

"She's not changing me. I still act like myself. I'm only helping her come to terms with this and not worry about what people are thinking of us."

The Velcro unfastening is liberation as the compress loosens its grip on my ribcage.

"That's still changing who you are, though." Sammy points out.

"I guess I'm hoping she'll stop feeling that way, you know? Like, if I do this for her, she'll eventually love me for me, and none of this will matter."

"This isn't cool, at all. Dump the pillow princess, and get yourself a real lesbian."

"Don't talk about my girl like that."

"Shut up!" Sammy raises her voice. "It's true. She's wack for even trying to change you."

Looking from outside of the relationship, I know this must seem insane, but she doesn't understand what we have. If pretending to be a guy means fewer confrontations, then I'm willing to do this for us.

Weeks after the talk I had with Sammy, Adelina's plan to transform me into "Tyler" intensifies. She takes it upon herself to replace my wardrobe with loose-fitting clothes and calling me by this new name on a full-time basis. Little by little, I'm acting more masculine. We've even stopped drawing attention to ourselves.

On a lazy Sunday morning, we lay scattered on her bed, planning for my birthday in two weeks.

"This thing is killing me. I can't believe I slept with it on." I unwrap my breasts, seeking relief.

Adelina's face goes blank when she sees me unbound. She stays quiet as tears fall.

"Are you okay?" I ask, confused. "Talk to me. What's up?"

"Your breasts are so perky. It's disgusting."

"Perky breasts are disgusting? I must've missed the memo."

"I'm serious, Tyler. How am I supposed to see you as my boyfriend with those? It's weird."

Maybe this is the talk we need for her to realize how mental this is. Then we can finally drop the charade.

"Would you get a breast reduction if I paid for it?" she sideswipes me.

"A what?"

"A breast reduction, or maybe even a full reconstructive surgery?"

"Please tell me this a joke."

This new request was not the trajectory I was hoping for. I bury my face into her pillow, trying to keep myself together. If she notices that I'm crying, it'll give her ammunition on how unconvincing I am as a man.

"What are you going to do with them, anyway? It's not like I suck on them." she gags.

The body-shaming turns my cheeks and ears red. Adelina is still crying, but her demeanor has changed. She's now in full persuasion mode.

"Baby, if you do a full female-to-male sex change, we can move to another state and start a new life together."

My face is still hidden. This feels like a bad dream.

"I would love you forever, Tyler." Adelina kisses my arm. "Can we please do this? I'll be your support system. I'll pay for the expenses and everything."

"How? That's thousands of dollars."

"I'll figure something out. Don't worry about that."

I pick my head up from the pillow.

"I'm not a guy, Adelina. You said this was for people to leave us alone, and they have."

"Exactly. Imagine if you went for the full package." her enthusiasm jumps up a few notches.

"You have it all figured out, huh? Why is it that I'm the only one making changes here?"

"That's not true. I'll be going through it with you. It won't be easy when we move, and I'll have to get used to the new you. We're in this together."

"This is… wow. I don't even know what to say to this. It's a lot to digest."

There's desperation growing in her. She kisses me again to keep me engaged in her proposition.

"Let's do some research and see how you feel about the process. Then we can make an informed decision."

"All right, look into it." I surrender.

"We'll go to the Center tomorrow. They should have all the information we need there."

As soon as Adelina stops talking about it, I ask her to sneak me out. Her family is moving around all parts of the house, so it's trickier than usual. I duck into her closet while she scopes things out.

The radio gets turned up to cover any noise coming from my hiding spot. Pink, the singer, vocalizes torment over toxic love through the speakers, singing *Just Like A Pill*. It feels like the song is about me, as I'm kept secret and forced back in the closet.

THE TRUTH ABOUT TRANS

The Center on 13th Street and 7th Avenue in New York City is a safe haven for our community. Anyone from any walk of life can come here to be educated, counseled, and entertained on sexuality and identity. A muscular man in clothes that are one size too small, greets us as we walk in. His charisma makes it forgivable.

"Good afternoon. Welcome to The Center. How may I help you beauties today?"

"Hi, I'm not sure who I need to speak to, but I'd

like to get information on a female-to-male transition," I explain to him.

"The on-site counselors can provide you with that information. We also have these pamphlets you can take with you. Give me a moment to see who is available." He gives me a few booklets that I stuff into my bag awkwardly, then picks up the phone receiver.

Adelina turns to me, "Let me see one of those pamphlets."

A different headline has gotten my attention as I pull it out of the plastic wall mount and read the content:

BE YOURSELF:

QUESTIONS & ANSWERS FOR LESBIAN, GAY BISEXUAL, TRANSGENDER, QUEER, INTERSEX, ASEXUAL, & PANSEXUAL YOUTH

"You *are* being yourself, Tyler," she says defensively.

I continue to ignore her. Another title stands out to me:

THE TRANSGENDER UMBRELLA

Adelina's tension loosens when she notices the brochure I'm eyeing. It's an umbrella with different terms listed under it. The description reads:

Transgender: An all-encompassing or umbrella term for people whose anatomies and/or appearances do not conform to predominant gender roles.

Under the umbrella are other terms:

Transsexual: One who is born into one gender but identifies as the opposite; (i.e., transitioning MTF or FTM. *May experience Gender Dysphoria.)

It makes me think of Brandon Teena's story. Did he know any of these terms existed, or did he live without ever knowing there were others like him?

Maybe this is where I would fall on the spectrum.

Cross-dresser, drag queen/king, bigender, androgyne, agender, genderqueer, and gender fluid are all defined here. I never knew there were so many different terms and identities other than straight, lesbian, gay, bisexual, and trans. None of these other terms help to identify what I feel, except maybe a cross-dresser. Shopping in the women's department stopped as soon as I turned eighteen.

"Remember that this is all new information. Give it time to sink in." Adelina encourages.

"One of our counselors just returned from a Transgender Workshop and says today is your lucky day. Follow this corridor to the second door on your left to Family Services. Ask to see Sarah Stoakes."

Inside Family Services, we're greeted by a dazzling male seahorse rocking a squared-off beard that emphasizes their jawline, full breasts, and a gender-neutral nameplate that reads Alex Morgan. Their deep voice has a rough underbelly, but the kindness in their eyes has a feminine tenderness. This person is an enigma as I'm unable to decipher what box the world would place them in. So, why am I trying to put them in one? Alex exudes a freedom I've been searching for. After directing us to Sarah's office, they give me a calendar of events for the month.

"We're having a meet-and-greet party next Saturday, if you're interested." They turn their attention to Adelina. "You should come, too."

She gives her signature fake half-smile as we turn to the next phase of this experience. The door to the counselor's office is open. I tap lightly to let the woman know we're here. Silver, short, spiked hair matches her trendy style.

"Hi, come in. Are you the one looking for information on FTM?" she confirms.

"Yes. I'm Tyler. This is my girlfriend, Adelina." I shake her hand.

"Soon to be fiancé," she adds.

"Can you tell me about yourself, Tyler?" she gestures for me to have a seat.

I'm not prepared to give any personal details. The only reason I'm here is for Adelina to finally come to her senses. Now that I'm sitting in front of a professional, I have no idea what to say. I thought I'd be the one asking questions.

"Um, I'm about to celebrate my twentieth birthday in a couple of weeks. I'm Puerto Rican, from the Bronx. I live with my parents and two siblings. An older brother and a younger sister. Yes, I'm the middle child." I laugh nervously.

"Happy early birthday to you," she smiles.

"I don't think that's what she means," Adelina adds.

"No, it's okay. These are things I'd like to know, as well," she turns back to me. "And how have these experiences shaped the way you identify in terms of gender? Have you always identified as a male?" the counselor continues.

"I've always been a tomboy. I wanted to be like my brother and cousins growing up and would wear their clothes."

"Well, that doesn't necessarily mean you're transgender. There's a growing list of terms and ways to identify. It's not a one size fits all thing."

"Yeah, I got some of those new terms from this." I hold up the Transgender Umbrella pamphlet.

"Based on what you know, what would you say your pronouns are?"

"Umm, she and her."

"Tyler wants more information on hormone therapy and top surgery to see if it's a good fit for him," Adelina interjects.

"Well, the first steps would be two mental health evaluations, then they would issue a letter of transition."

"Mental health evaluation?" I ask defensively.

"It's based on international guidelines for transgender care when Sex Reassignment Surgery or Gender Affirmation Surgery is considered. These requirements allow for a more comprehensive, clinical view for anyone seeking a transition letter, which would begin the pre-operative preparation phase. The objective is to minimize regret once the surgery is complete, as it can impact your life in many unforeseen ways. It also addresses gender concerns and safeguarding against social adjustment post-operation."

"Are there pills or medications that I need to take?" I don't have health insurance, so this matters.

Adelina reaches out for my hand and places it on her lap. She's tapping her leg anxiously.

"In this case, it would be hormone replacement therapy. It's used to induce physical changes caused by puberty. Doctors usually start their patients with a low dose, then safely increase that dosage over a couple of months. It could be administered through injection, patches, pellets, pills, or a topical gel. It may help reduce psychological or emotional distress, and improve quality of life for those suffering from gender dysphoria."

Sarah pulls out a handbook outlining all the changes that could happen during transition. There are pictures of naked women with parts of their bodies circled as target areas affected by testosterone. The following pages detail these modifications, which could take three to ten years to reach full potential. Within the first six months, the person will notice a deepening in their voice, clitoral enlargement, body fat redistribution, interruption of the menstrual cycle, a difference in the hairline, and an increase in facial and pubic hair.

"You will meet regularly with a specialist to document physical developments, monitor dosage, and to observe your behavioral health, as well as proper supplementation of calcium and Vitamin D, following age-appropriate recommendations for cisgender men."

"Would I have to legally change my name and gender?"

"Of course, you do, silly. You can't go around with a name like Solei, looking like Jose." Adelina jokes.

"Excuse me. Please let me answer the questions."

The counselor rolls her eyes at Adelina.

"No, you're not obligated to do so. Every choice in this matter is yours. How far you go is up to you," she continues. "I will say, though, that I've seen people have serious problems and scandals when the paperwork isn't updated to reflect their truth."

I flip through the handbook to avoid eye contact. The following section is titled:

Chest Reconstruction (Top Surgery)

Before and after pictures show surgeries performed on female-to-male patients, where they shaped the skin and tissue to match the contour of a male chest. Scars are strategically hidden under pec muscles. The nipples and areolas get resized with new positions to look more masculine. The following page has illustrations of phalloplasty, a surgery that consists of the construction or reconstruction of a penis.

"You see this?" I show the images to Adelina, shaking my head with absolute certainty that this isn't meant for me.

"Based on what I've seen and heard during our meeting, I don't think this will solve whatever you two are going through. An uninformed decision could lead down a destructive and lonely path, especially if you're altering to please someone else. You'd be surprised at how people, who supposedly love you, will be quick to leave when things get too real for them. This could cause alienation from everyone and everything in your life." The counselor closes the book before I continue gawking, with a matter-of-fact look that tells me we're done here.

An art piece on the wall draws my attention. It's a peach that has been bitten into with juices overflowing. The words written within say:

"For a long time, I thought I wanted to be a nun. Then I realized what I really wanted to be was a lesbian."

-Mabel Maney

I can't help but chuckle at the timeliness of this quote.

"Thank you for your honesty, Ms. Stoakes. That was exactly what I was hoping to hear."

This meeting has officially freed me from the trap I've allowed myself to be caged into. Unburdened by a cross that isn't mine to bear, my head bows in gratitude while walking out. Adelina stays behind.

Outside of Family Services, there's a beautiful garden that I paid no mind to on the way in. A small bridge with a pond underneath connects to another part of the garden. I decide to wait on a bench between the two buildings. The sunlight on my skin and the sounds creating an acoustic bounce ground me to the earth. My eyes open when a shadow moves in. Adelina is standing there, blocking the sun's love.

"I got a list of psychiatrists who can evaluate you if you're still down to move forward."

The gurgling of the water behind us provides comfort against the harshness of her persistence.

"Adelina, I'm not going through with this. I'm not even going to do Tyler anymore. I've never wanted to be a man. You know that."

"You've said it yourself; you have always been a tomboy."

"We both know that's not the same thing. That woman just confirmed it. I don't want a penis or facial hair or to cut my tits off. I don't want any of that.

"I can't... be a lesbian, Tyler. I'm not a lesbian." Adelina starts to have another meltdown.

"Look, I can pretend to be Tyler for a little longer, but eventually you have to come to terms with the fact that you're in love with a woman."

Adelina stays quiet.

"Is it really that bad? So bad, you would subject me to a lifetime of hormones and surgeries against what I want for myself. I can't do it. I can't self-sacrifice for you, anymore."

"Then don't do that part, baby. You can wear a strap-on when we go out," she goes into seduction mode. "My man's bulge needs to be well endowed, anyway."

"Holy shit. Are you kidding me? Is this a hidden camera show or something?"

"Okay, how about just a few hormone shots to deepen your voice and grow some hair?"

"No, I'm done." I declare once and for all.

Those images in the binder fuel a new determination. You don't transform your body like that to silence someone else's beast.

"What she said isn't true. I wouldn't leave you no matter what." Adelina's continued bargaining keeps her in denial.

"Then why not accept me the way I am? Stop trying to change me."

"That's not fair. You know how important this is to me."

"You know what's not fair? For you to expect me to rearrange my entire identity because *you're not a lesbian.* You don't even have to say all of that, bring me around, and they'll get it. For all you know, they won't even care."

Adelina buries her face into my neck.

"I care. I don't want the world thinking I'm something that I'm not. I don't even consider myself bisexual. You're the only girl I like, and look at you. You're practically a boy!"

"Why does this have to be so complicated? You love me, and I love you back. Why can't that be enough?"

"You don't know how my family is. They'll disown me! Do you think we'll live happily ever after if I tell my parents?"

Tears stream down her face. It seems like all I ever do now is make her cry.

"We won't!" she continues. "I'm not losing my family for you, so you better figure this out."

Adelina walks away without turning back. I stay in the garden listening to the sounds until a light rain starts to dampen my skin. The train ride on the northbound car is congested. My eyes look at nothing but observe everything.

A parallel reality plays out in my mind – a world where I give into Adelina's request. What would people think? My parents would be disturbed. My brother and sister would probably be freaked out and ban me from seeing their future kids. People would know something is off from a mile away but not put their finger on it. It already happens to me because it's not my truth. How can I convince them when I haven't convinced myself? And no amount of hormones can undo that glimpse when you look into the eyes of a woman that loves being a woman.

"There goes my boyfriend, Tyler Love." Adelina's slogan infiltrates my thoughts.

A homeless man crosses over from the next subway car.

"Excuse me, ladies and gentlemen, sorry for the interruption. I'm not here to beg for money," he speaks with the cadence of a poet. "I'm a Vietnam vet and the homeless philosopher. Some call me a prophet. Others call me a nigga, but I'm neither. I just listen to things that pass through, is all."

He walks up and down the car while speaking, engaging attention as he does. Almost everyone is listening intently.

"I'm here to share my wisdom and ideas with anyone who will hear me out. If you are present here on this train. Right now. I have but one question. Do you know who you are? Not who others think you are. You know, those other people we become in our daily lives? Yeah, not that. You. You, when it's just you and you. And no, them." his sermon has us hooked. "No, he. No, she. No, they be. If you are present here on this train. Right now. I have only one thought to share. Stupid is as stupid does, does happen when you're stupidly doing what everyone else does."

We all laugh with him.

"If you are present here on this train. Right now. I have but one solution. Figure out who you are and be the biggest, baddest motherfucker on this planet. Thank you.

I accept coins, bills, food donations, books, and smiles."

The homeless philosopher jazzes up the last line in deep, smooth, Barry White-like inflections. He holds a hat to his heart and graciously collects donations dropped into it, showing genuine appreciation for each one. When he gets to my side of the train, we smile big at each other – kindred spirits, and we know it.

He comes in closer and whispers, "Don't do it. Whatever it is, don't do it."

"What?"

"To be honest, miss, I don't know. Just don't do it."

He faces the car doors and mimics the *ting tung* sound as it chimes. The homeless philosopher exits without saying another word. His message resonates, but I shake the coincidence off. There's no way he channeled it from beyond. That probably could have applied to anyone on this train. A woman sitting across from me – who may have heard his advice – is watching as I prepare to get off at the next stop.

A sticky heat has everyone in the hood out on every corner. The *Ruff Ryders' Anthem* is blasting from a car driving by. Roaring motorcycle mufflers pop into action, and screaming kids run in and out of park sprinklers. There's a distinct contrast between this summertime joy and the sadness in my soul. It all creates a weight that induces a sluggish need for sleep. A nap would be the perfect getaway from these feelings of being an alien in my skin. My walk is different. The clothes I wear and this hair are unrecognizable. Nothing feels the same anymore. The person that reflects in mirrors and pictures hasn't looked like me in a long time.

A group of guys huddled up into a lyrical cipher are challenging each other to see who can create the most complex metaphors. On a different day, I would check to see who I know and join the sidelines as a hype man.

Today though, I shrink into myself instead. After passing safely and without drawing their attention, another hurdle appears. On the opposite side of the yard is a group of girls in high energy. Some are getting their hair braided, others are double-dutching, and the rest are talking loud and cracking jokes.

"What's up, Slim Shady!" one of them yells out.

Damn. It's hard to keep a low profile when everybody and their mother are out in the neighborhood you grew up in, especially when you walk around with a bleach blonde head of hair. Instead of stopping, I pick up the pace a little. It could be anyone, friend or foe. The girl's voice calls out again, this time from directly behind me.

"Solei."

My defenses are up as I spin around.

"You don't know people anymore?"

A familiar face that I haven't seen in a while smiles back. It's Camila. Yes, *that* Camila. My ex-girlfriend.

The last person to leave me with a broken heart. We throw arms around each other in a bear hug. The warmth feels like we've lost no time at all.

"What are you up to?" I deflect.

"I'm getting my hair braided for a play. Do you have plans later? Tonight's our opening night. I would love for you to be there. It starts at 9 p.m."

"What's it about?" I ask before committing to open fresh wounds.

"Well, it's called *Devil May Care*. It's about a teenage girl that lives in a homeless shelter in the Lower East Side. She saves people's lives based on these visions she sees until a dirty cop starts to blackmail her." Camila's passion for the story is gleaming in her eyes.

"Is your boyfriend gonna be there?"

"I don't have a boyfriend anymore." she smiles.

"Interesting... well, I would love to support your opening night. I'll be there."

I calculate the time in my head. That desperately needed nap will have to happen on the train ride back into the city. There's no way I'm turning down a night out with her.

After the show, we go for dinner and drinks at a spot I know we won't get carded.

"That was incredible! When did you get into acting?" I gush over her.

"Believe it or not, I got my heart broken. That guy I was dating cheated on me with one of the girls from church, and I was devastated."

"Wait, how long was that happening for? Who did he hook up with from church?"

"With Jessica, for almost a year. Goes to show that not even a God-fearing man can keep it in his pants, and he was older than me. He knew exactly how to play it."

"That's pretty bold. How does someone keep that

secret when you all go to the same church? Did you ever suspect anything?"

"Never. And yes, the fuck he was. I would've bet my life on his loyalty. He had me and my mother fooled."

It's bittersweet hearing that the man her mother was happy to see Camila with cheated and broke her heart. I try to find satisfaction in this but can't.

"How old is he?"

"Thirty-five, with a Benz, and a summer home in the Poconos. I was ready to marry him and everything." Camila downs the rest of her drink and sorrows.

My jealousy has me doing the same. Her mother accepted anyone, as long as it wasn't me. The waiter returns just in time with our next round.

"I hope his dick falls off," she laughs with tears in her eyes.

"To dickless ex-boyfriends." I raise my glass.

Camila gladly raises hers to mine.

"Anyways… a friend signed me up to this improv class, and that was it. I fell in love with theater. Who would've thought? Me, a theater nerd?"

Heartbreak. The great catalyst to better versions of ourselves. Maybe that's why I went through this with Adelina. What is she bringing me closer to?

"Have you dated anyone since we… you know, stopped seeing each other?" she avoids eye contact.

I've managed to leave Adelina's name out of the entire dinner until now. Thinking of her makes my stomach turn.

"There's this one girl from Queens. We've been dating since February, but it's not working out."

I keep it simple, hoping it's enough to satisfy her curiosity.

"Since February? It must be serious then. That's like five years in lesbian time. What is she like?"

"I thought it was getting serious, but it's also been

getting weird lately."

"Weird how?"

"I don't know. The first couple of months were amazing. Now she's trying to change everything about me."

"I see. The classic, 'I love you, you're perfect, now change' syndrome. It happens to the best of us," Camila jokes.

"This was my first real relationship after us. No disrespect, but our relationship was childish compared to this one. I don't know how to get her to stop trying to make me into something I'm not."

"Don't give in. No matter what. Make her love you the way you are."

"I don't think it's going to be so simple. She's not asking for minor adjustments."

"Is that why you look different? The hair and the clothes. Is this all for her?"

"Kind of, but not entirely. The hair was something I did in the heat of the moment, a rebellion sort of thing. But she's encouraged a more masculine vibe. *Encouraged* being a mild understatement."

"It can't be that bad. You're not that far out of your comfort zone, right?"

Camila's search for silver linings has always been her thing. I take a deep breath and center myself before revealing my awkward situation.

"Please keep this between us, Camila. Like 'take it to the grave' type shit, okay?"

"I promise. What's up? Are you good?"

"My girlfriend wants me to have a sex change so we can live like a straight couple."

Camila spits out her drink.

"I was expecting a threesome or anal. You know, something freaky. But not an actual freak show being forced into a sex change!" she cleans off the beer from her face. "Sol, what the hell?"

"*Hello*, I know. This is my reality."

"I've never heard of some shit like that. You're not thinking of doing it, are you?"

"Not really, but I've been going along with it. I was hoping she would get over the fantasy, but she hasn't."

"You need to get out of that relationship ASAP! Run for your life and never look back."

Camila reinforces the conclusion that's been disturbing my brain since I left The Center.

"You shouldn't have to go through all of that for her to love you. There are plenty of women that will accept you for who you are. Believe that!" Camila gestures for the check.

A part of me is still hopeful that Adelina is on the other side of town, coming to her senses.

LAST CALL

By the time I get back home, it's still early for a Friday night. The house is calm, except for my parents sitting at the dining table with concerned looks on their faces.

"Who died?" I try to make a joke about the somber mood.

"Take your hat off," Mami demands.

I do as she asks without question. This has become a sort of ceremony between us as the "you cut your hair" argument, followed by examining my hairline.

When I do come home with a fresh cut, we have a showdown, and I get the silent treatment for days.

"Adelina called looking for you today," Mami finally reveals.

I'm automatically uptight. It's not common for my mother to share information when someone calls for me, especially Adelina.

"Okay, what did she say?"

Mami stares me down, then sits without saying another word. My father takes over and tries to mediate the situation.

"Sol, sit down. We need to talk about something."

My heart pounds with so much intensity that I'm on the verge of a heart attack. Did something happen to Adelina?

"First things first, I don't want that girl anywhere near my house." Mami finally breaks the silence.

"Um," confused, and now a little less worried, I

respond, "okay…"

"Yolanda, why don't we start with what she told you?" my father says.

"You guys are scaring me. What's this all about?"

"That girl had the nerve to tell me that I have to take down your Sweet Sixteen picture because you look too much like a girl. *¿Esa 'ta loca?* This is my house!" Mami yells.

The picture in question is a 24x28 framed portrait of me in a tiara and an off-white dress my aunt from Puerto Rico designed. My parents paid $300 to have it framed for all who visit. It's a symbol of the daughter they once had. A naive version before the runaway, the sex worker, and the little dyke pretending to be a boy.

"I'm not taking that picture down!" Mami rages on.

"Shh, lower your voice. I don't want the neighbors knowing our business," Papi demands. "Solei, I feel like I don't know you anymore. What's going on?"

"She also told me that you're having a sex change,"

my mother adds.

They both watch my face for a reaction – which has undoubtedly gone pale.

"She told you that?"

The burden of them knowing my secret humbles me.

"Yes, and she told me about the surgery to remove your *tetas*. That you're going to take pills to be more like a man." Mami erupts again.

Her anger has mutated into fear and concern. I can't believe Adelina would take it this far, especially after everything that happened today.

"Solei, we want you to go for therapy," Papi says. "To help you make sense of things."

"This is some bullshit, Papi! You guys made this decision based on things that *she* told you? Things that were her idea in the first place." I yell at my father.

The summer heat is instigating my resentment.

"Don't scream at your father." Mami charges back,

pouncing from her seat.

Papi stands between us in reaction to my mother's aggression. He puts his hands on her shoulders and tries to calm her. My response is to kick into fight-or-flight mode. I choose the latter and flee before my parents can continue their interrogation.

Sammy welcomes me with a hug and a beer when I show up an emotional wreck at her door.

"Yo, let's get some blow," I tell her, ready to escape these feelings.

"Nah, I'm good with my six-pack. I don't wanna mess with that tonight."

"Well, can you hit up your connect for me?"

Sammy unwillingly makes the call. My goodies get delivered in less than ten minutes, and the staircase becomes our chill spot while I do bumps. Once the nasal drip comes down, I start to feel like Superman – which always makes me more talkative, and I begin to tell her about Camila.

"Oh my God. Do you think you guys are getting back together?" Sammy questions.

"It's not even like that. Camila is different now. . After everything that happened with her mom and that guy she dated, the church, everything. There's no turning back."

"Yeah, but she's legal now. It's a different battlefield, and I bet she still loves you."

"Touché. I just don't think it's like that anymore. She's going through her own relationship drama."

"Shut up and work your magic. Ever since you got with Adelina, you've lost your *mojo*. You doubt yourself too much." Sammy straightens her back and speaks with a faux British accent, "it's very unbecoming of you."

Hearing her name reminds me of everything that played out today. Then a flash of my parent's faces makes my stomach turn. I drink and take more bumps to bypass reality. My vision blurs the deeper I go into the void. This crossover to the other side of intoxication convinces me to call Adelina. When she doesn't pick up her cellphone, I call the house. Her mother picks up after too many rings.

"Adelina, please." I slur.

"Do you know what time it is?" she reprimands.

"It's an emergency, Señora."

"Well, she's not here anyway. She's at Jesenia's. What's your name? I'll tell her in the morning."

"My name *ish* Solei. Tell her I don't want to be her boyfriend anymore." I hang up, then take another bump.

My sense of consequence diminishes the further I spiral.

"Should I call Jesenia?"

"Hell yeah," Sammy instigates.

Jesenia answers after a few rings.

"Hey, it's Sol. Put Adelina on the phone."

"You have some nerve calling me at this time."

"I know it's late, but it's not like you're sleeping anyway. Can I speak to her, please?"

"She's not here, Sol."

"I know she is! Her mother told me."

"I'm just a decoy, babe. An excuse for her mother not to worry. Your woman was getting that money for you to finally become a man, but I guess that's not happening anymore."

"What's that supposed to mean? Where is she?"

"You don't know?" Jesenia taunts. "The girl you're so in love with, whose name you got tattooed… and you don't know what she's doing in the middle of the night? *Tsk, tsk.*"

Inebriation takes over as she continues.

"You chose the wrong girl, Solei. See how I'm home being a good girl? While the one you picked is shaking her ass in the strip club."

"What?"

Jesenia laughs in a cruel, Cruella De Vil kind of way, "Oops, maybe I wasn't supposed to say anything."

"Why are you making shit up to mess with my head?"

"You wish I was. Too bad your relationship is over now that Adelina knows you're a fake. It's time for a real man in her life. I knew she wasn't gay."

I hang up before she can say anything more, then begin to connect the dots, and wonder how long Adelina has been a stripper. She continued to spend money freely, even after we stopped working at TLC. Whenever I asked how she was able to, she would brush it off and say her father's trading company was doing well. I believed her even though they had a beat-up minivan parked in the driveway. The signs were all there. Her shoe collection just kept growing. Plus, the way she's been dressing lately and posing for pictures. Now to find out, this was how she was planning to fund the surgery.

It's 1 a.m. when I leave Sammy's on a mission to Queens. Halfway there, a realization comes to mind. What if Adelina goes to Jesenia's at the end of the night? I hadn't thought about that in my rash decision to leave the Bronx. There's no turning back now, though. I'll take my chances and hope she comes home instead. A gravitational pull keeps me going one foot after the other to the corner of her block.

Even though the bedroom lights are off, little rocks get thrown, in hopes she pops her head out. Nothing. My walk continues to avoid looking suspicious. On the way back down, I start to check car doors. A few tries later, a couple of houses down from Adelina's, an unlocked car becomes my temporary shelter. My inner detective watches each headlight that drives by.

What am I going to say when I see her? I was so intent on getting here that I have no clue what my objective is.

After waiting the most drawn-out hours of my life, a black BMW pulls up to the front of Adelina's house and parks. My entire being sinks like an anchor has just dropped off the side of me. When no one comes out, I emerge from the borrowed car in a slow and steady prowl. My adrenaline is pumping at full speed. Adelina is sitting on the passenger side, making out with some random man in the driver's seat. My first instinct is to punch the window as hard as I can. She jumps and turns to face me.

"Get out of the car!" I yell while slamming against the glass repeatedly. Adelina then motions for the driver to take off. He shifts the car into gear. Just before they peel off, I jump on the front, gripping at the edges of the hood.

"What are you doing?" Adelina screams through

the glass.

Tires screech into a turn—my body slams on the concrete. The impact cracks against my kneecap and scrapes my elbow. I tumble and roll to a stop. The sidewalk becomes a resting place as I sit in disbelief. Shortly after, heels pounding the pavement walk in my direction. Adelina turns the corner.

"Are you okay?" she asks.

"I'm fantastic, Adelina. Never better."

I dust myself off.

"What are you doing here?"

"You don't get to ask questions when you just pulled up in some dude's car." I snap. "And you were kissing him? Who was that?"

"I don't need to explain myself. You did this when you decided you didn't want to be Tyler!"

"You're right. It doesn't even matter anymore. But why did you tell my mother all those things? Why are you trying to ruin my life?"

"Lower your voice. You're going to wake people up."

"Are you kidding me? You disrupt my entire life, and you expect me to be thoughtful of your neighbors?"

"Solei, please. Calm down."

"Don't ever call my house or look for me again."

I walk away, leaving Adelina and all the bullshit she put me through behind. The ride back home is just as long as the night has been. My reflection on the train car door looks sickly from dilated pupils and swollen, bloodshot eyes with dirty clothes after being thrown off the car. It's broad daylight when I get back to the Bronx.

Each key gets slipped in slowly to avoid making noise, but the chain is latched when I push open the door. Now I have to ring the bell to get in. If I know anything about my mother, it's that she's very deliberate when she does things like this. Whatever time I arrived, we were going to finish our talk. The sound of the doorbell sets off barking from the dog first. When Mami reaches the front door, she unleashes her wrath, breaking things all over the house. Her screaming and cursing lead to kicking me out of the house once more – the barrage of insults shreds my already wounded spirit. By the time Papi comes down, the kitchen has become a combat zone. The blame is now being projected onto him.

"This is your fault, Kelvin. Look at her! *¡Quiere ser un macho!*" she screams as she shatters a dish on the floor.

My worn-out eyes burn from the salt of tears. I walk back out of the house and lay down in the middle of the road, hoping for a car to speed through and not notice me until it's too late. There's peace with this being the end of my life. The comfort puts me into a deep sleep right where I am. When my consciousness returns, police officers and EMT workers are surrounding me. Mami cries for them to leave me alone while

Papi is being asked a series of questions.

"Ma, what's happening?" I ask when I realize that I'm strapped to the stretcher.

She's unable to talk through her sobs. Papi answers me in a low voice.

"They're going to admit you for a psychiatric hold because they think you tried to kill yourself. You're going to get the help you need, *muñeca*." Papi takes out his handkerchief and wipes his eyes.

EMT workers take me away.

90 Days Later...

After almost three months of sleeping at a rehab facility, my own weeping wakes me up again. I still don't recognize the bare white walls. I'm drenched in sweat and breathing rapidly. The seventy-two hour hold I was placed under for psychiatric evaluation resulted in ninety days at the Five Elements Rehab Center.

This morning is the last session with my therapist, Ms. Takara. The meeting is brief and ends with her handing me my paperwork and release forms.

"You have to bring these documents to the county clerk's office. Once you do that, your program is officially complete, and they will close your case."

"Thank you so much." I shake her hand as a free woman.

My parents drive me home with my mother's evil dog, Sammy sitting in the back. I'm actually kind of happy to see the little fucker. He declares a truce by lying next to me and taking a deep sigh. His eyes avert back and forth, making sure I don't try anything.

Winnie greets me in the front yard with "Welcome Home" balloons and a banner when we pull up. The rest of my family and friends jump out, yelling, "SUR-PRISE!" when I get inside.

"I didn't know you were throwing me a party."

"You know Mami and Papi take any opportunity to throw a party." Winnie jokes.

Sammy runs up and gives me a bear hug.

"I have a surprise for you."

She pulls me through aunts, uncles, and cousins, showering me in hugs and kisses until we reach the backyard. Her girlfriend, Natalia, is sitting on a lounge chair next to a certain someone.

"Hey, stranger." Camila smiles.

"I went through a lot to track this girl down for your party," Sammy says proudly.

"That's so crazy. I had a dream with you last night." I admit.

Camila blushes.

"I don't mean it like that... it wasn't sexual or anything."

"Oh, shucks. I could use some action these days." she teases.

"Seriously, though. You kept trying to save me but couldn't. I was sinking into quicksand while you were frantically looking for something to pull me up with. It happened twice, and both times I died."

"Well, damn. That's morbid," Sammy says.

"There's this website that interprets dreams. Let me see what it says. I'll check quicksand first." Camila then reads the description: "To dream that you are sinking in quicksand indicates feelings of insecurity. You have misjudged the solid foundation you are on. You need to pay attention to what you are doing and where you are going."

"That could mean something, right?"

"Let's see what it says under death," she continues. "To die in your dream symbolizes inner changes, transformation, self-discovery, and positive developments that are happening within you or your life," she pauses and stares into my eyes. "You're moving on to new beginnings, leaving the past behind you."

"The accuracy, though!" Sammy chimes in.

"Okay, that one definitely means something," I confirm.

Camila smirks and pulls an envelope from her purse.

"I got you a present."

A gift certificate to a writer's workshop is taped on the inside of a card that reads:

I remember when we were together, you would write the most beautiful poems and short stories. This is my way of paying it forward with the gift of creativity. May these classes spark something within you that brings you closer

to your higher self. -Camila

"Cheers to your rebirth, Solei Romero."

ACKNOWLEDGEMENTS

A decade has passed since the first edition of this book was written, under the title Adelina's Perfect Girl. During this time, the collective growth we have gone through has been beautiful yet tragic. Some friendships have fallen off, because when you're young, everyone is your friend, but then life happens, and you find yourself with only a handful of confidantes. This, too, has been a beautiful yet tragic experience.

I will start once again by thanking the creative energies of the Universe. The force that flows within us and pushes us to – do that thing you've been thinking about – is a profound act when you give it your full attention and manifest what is channeling through you. I will continue to answer the call. It's the only thing that makes the solitude of this work bearable. On that note, I'd like to say thank you to my ancestors for fueling my dreams' momentum while protecting me from the world, your guidance is felt in the whispers of the wind.

Thank you to the love of my life and the greatest adventure I've ever been a part of; Stephanie Barquero. One of the best decisions I've ever made was to create that vision board a week before meeting you! Everything I asked for, I have found in you, and it blows my mind on a regular basis. Thank you for the hours of edits and being with me in the trenches to make this little book match how I saw it in my mind's eye. Thank you for believing in me, in us, and in this thing we're building together. You're the stuff dreams are made of.

To my parents and siblings, thank you for the gift of tough love growing up. It has helped me to grow a thick skin and survive anything this world throws at me. As the "problem child" of the family, I know I've given you many headaches and sleepless nights. You may question my choices at times, but you have never given up on me. In the end, that was exactly what I needed to flourish. To my beautiful nieces, Chelsie and Hailey, I'm so proud to be your titi, and I'm grateful to watch you grow into your own identities. May you love yourself in ways that force the people around you to match that energy. And to my in-laws, Terri and Eddie. Thanks for loving our crazy family! We love you back.

Special thanks to the photographer, Paulina Bar-asch, the model that embodied a "young Slim" for the cover, Sacha Selhi, and Madel Hidalgo, for helping me to focus on a trans-friendly portrayal of my brush with this reality. The trans community deserves to be represented with love and respect as we create new worlds and better stories that include all of us. I promise to be mindful of the work I'm creating and the ways in which we are all portrayed.

To all the beautiful humans that are still part of my story after this wild ride called life, I love you and thank you for all the manifestations you bring into my world. May we continue to make beautiful memories until our teeth fall out and the wheels fall off.

AUTHOR BIOGRAPHY

Writer and independent filmmaker, Meriam Rodriguez, is a South Bronx native that has created and performed in various mediums throughout the New York

City underground for the past twenty years. The city's harshness has shaped an identity of activism coupled with a love of storytelling. From theater, writing, and spoken word, to grinding as a production assistant, she has continuously worked her way up the ladder. Meriam's work seeks to identify and heal from the human condition with all the ways we come up short of our ideologies. She has studied the filmmaking craft at every level to form an intrinsic understanding of the journey we set out to create.

Her earlier work includes a novel titled *Adelina's Perfect Girl* (2012), honored with a new look and title in this edition of *Identity Interrupted* (2021). Meriam has since worked on different sets for film and television productions, filming in the city and tri-state area. She started as a production assistant, learned the craft, and made her way into the Art Department. Her credits include *Uncut Gems, Clifford the Big Red Dog,*

Russian Doll, High Fidelity, and more. In between productions, she produces independent short films and documentaries under her own production company, Making Vintage Productions.

Meriam's short film *Be My Baby* (2021) poses the question, where do you draw the line in the manipulation of science and technology to solve our problems, and who has the right to make that decision – with Marina and Jose facing their individual realities of infertility, and her determination to go an unconventional route that seems to trigger everyone around her, this question becomes the catalyst in one woman›s fight for motherhood.

In 2013 she co-produced, co-wrote, and featured in a spoken word performance for *Soledad Speaks*. A journey that begins on the island of Puerto Rico and ends in modern-day New York City. Revisiting the colonization of an island, the effects on its women, and their journey from slavery, to rebellion, to freedom, Soledad Speaks' paid homage to those who came before us in hopes of understanding how their legacy has defined who we are today.

Meriam has also performed in different cities, venues, and colleges, including the legendary Nuyorican Poets Café, Camaradas, La Pregunta, The Bowery Poetry Club, *HISPANIC PANIC!*, Bronx Academy of Arts and Dance (BAAD!), Hostos, and more since 2006. Her travels also include performances in the plays *Jose Can Speak* and *Pink: The Chronicles of BC Jenny*.